6

An Otter

Underwater eyes, an eel's
Oil of water body. Neither fish nor beast is the otter:
Four legged yet water-gifted, to outfish fish;
With webbed feet and long ruddering tail
And a round head like an old tomcat.

Brings the legend of himself
From before wars or burials, in spite of hounds and vermin-poles:
Does not take root like the badger. Wanders, cries;
Gallops along land he no longer belongs to;
Re-enters the water by melting.

Of neither water nor land. Seeking
Some world lost when first he dived, that he cannot come at since,
Takes his changed body into holes of lakes;
As if blind, cleaves the stream's push till he licks
The pebbles of the source; from the sea

To sea crosses in three nights
Like a king in hiding. Crying to the old shape of the starlit land,
Over sunken farms. Crying to the old shape of the starlit land,
Without answer. Till light and birdsong come
Walloping up roads with the milk wagon.

Ted Hughes

LEARNING. ···············**services**

01579 372213

Duchy College Stoke Climsland
Learning Centre

This resource is to be returned on or before the last date
stamped below. To renew items please contact the Centre

Three Week Loan

16 RETURNED 2004

RETURNED 6

1/8 APR 2012 CANCELLED

Stormforce

David Chaffe

Stormforce Publications
Weare Giffard
Devon

First Published in 1999 by
Stormforce Publications
Little Weare Cottage
Weare Giffard
Devon
EX39 4QZ

©David Chaffe 1999
2nd printing 2001
1st paperback edition 2002
2nd printing 2003

599.7692/CHA

Stormforce

David Chaffe

Printed and bound in the EC by
R. Booth Ltd
Mabe
Penryn
Cornwall TR10 9HH

For all, but more particularly children, who also seek
understanding between humans and other animals

Gavin Maxwell

for Helen and Olivia,
with my love, always

for my father and mother
with my gratitude, always

Contents

© Gabrielle Bordewich

Stormforce is a happy and ongoing story.
It records how Storm, and other often, people
and events have so enriched my life.

Another small but significant step forward
for the most important cause of all

Jonathon Porritt

THE BEGINNING

North-West Devon during the winter of 1990-91

F or the young bitch otter it had been a long winter with cold
wet days and nights passing slowly. Then she had ventured
abroad only to complete the daily necessities of life.

She had been born one of twin cubs to an old female who was
unlikely to breed again, but who was still securely established on
the upper reaches of the River Torridge in the 'Land of the Two
Rivers'. She had been left much against her will along with her
sibling brother. Their old and experienced mother had regularly
brought her previous litters to the estuary margins close to the sea
whenever she felt it was time for the break-up of the family unit.

The young female had found it difficult to secure a secluded
holt, somewhere that was not only away from prying eyes but
which also kept her close to a waterway, a ditch or rhyne, or the
top of a tidal creek in order to give her the most immediate and
natural route of escape should she deem it necessary. Her mother
had expressly forewarned both of her cubs to keep that particular
ace card immediately to hand. Instead, by necessity, her home
had been above ground in dense blackthorn cover close to a group
of alders which were a rather noticeable landmark in this treeless
land.

Nevertheless, as she matured, the otter had grown accustomed
to the solitude of this ancient marsh. At dusk and at dawn on
crisp dry nights she had loved to explore the rough grass of the
marsh's wide expanses. Grazed by a thousand sheep, it faded into
the sea wall, the sea wall into salting, and salting into mudflat. At
high water the mudflats melted into snaking creeks and she had
enjoyed her first real freedom in the flat and shining estuary.

At first she had been fearful of her survival, especially since

11

one cold and particularly foggy February night she had lost contact with her brother. He had not returned from one of their joint forays in the estuary together; she had last seen and heard him as he fished towards the bar and the open sea. Had he not heeded their mother's advice of always staying away from man even though their paths would by necessity cross from time to time? Had he been over inquisitive of a homeward-bound trawler which had been crabbing off Hartland and Lundy? The crew were waiting for the right state of the tide to bring the boat quayside in order to unload the catch of shellfish. Had her brother been falsely lured contrary to his mother's cautioning by accepting the free meals being thrown overboard as the crew made ready for landing?

A few nights later she had checked his holt again. It was close to the only farmhouse on the marsh. The farm buildings were girded by stunted trees, the only ones left standing in these windswept, roadless and houseless pastures. There was no sign of him, no fresh or even relatively recent spraint, and thereafter his home, lost amongst a mêlée of countless roots, had remained unoccupied.

Meanwhile, although lonely, the bitch had found company in her winter neighbours. The teal and wigeon would tuck in behind the high seawall on chilly winter evenings mewing like cats. She welcomed the closeness of the lapwings and the black-headed gulls as they paddled in the nearby shallows and the snipe that probed the wet flashes for worms. She grew accustomed to the short-eared owls overhead as they quartered on lazy wingbeats the rank tussocks for their prey. But much nearer to her holt she relied on the company of the wintering flock of redwings that sought shelter in the hawthorn thicket. They were predominantly silent birds but also alongside her was the resident family of ever inquisitive and chattering wrens. The otter did not realise at that moment in time but the wren's scolding alarm call, reminiscent of a bunch of keys being rattled and always expressed at the first sign of danger, was to play an important role in her own family's survival in the months ahead.

During the short winter days the duck had been choosing partners, and now as the daylight hours lengthened so did the urge to return to their summer breeding grounds. The otter recalled more of her mother's words. She was now nearly twenty months of age, alone, and quietly she had experienced her first major hormonal change. So if she was to fulfill the joy of motherhood she was going to have to finally break the still tenuous bond between her mother and herself. She had occasionally recognised her mother's distinctive call above the wind since their parting. Now more importantly she had to sever the bond with the 'Land of the Two Rivers', and in particular any thoughts of returning to the upper reaches of the Torridge valley, her birthplace.

She would have to travel far to establish her own territory by taking advantage of the prevailing westerly winds and currents along the north Devon shore of the Bristol Channel. As soon as the earliest chiffchaffs were passing through, and there were the first signs of elvers making their runs into the creeks, she would quickly be on her way.

During her spring journey she chose several temporary homes, often seeking shelter in natural rock crevices under the steep cliffs, but always trying to stay as close as possible to the high water mark for safety. Her diet was now almost entirely of marine fish, and only occasionally would she venture ashore.

By springtime she had discovered a stream issuing through a high shingle ridge with freshwater ditches lying behind the seawall. The area reminded her of the original marsh to which she had been brought by her mother and she quickly established herself following the same patterns and techniques taught to her by her mother before her departure.

The otter was now wiser. She gave herself the opportunity of creating alternative bolts and couches; she had one particular favourite reedbed, its watery exit affording her easy access to and from the estuary of the Severn. In the stream's flow she would catch her favourite food, silver eels, and in the density of the phragmites reedbeds she sheltered from the last of the chill winter winds. She was safe there. She learned the vagaries of the tides on a coastline providing the world's second highest tide-fall and she watched the world's last mud-horse fisherman who worked the very low-water limit of the west Somerset shore for his catch. A wooden sledge is pulled out across the mud to long, sock-like nets staked in the tidal race with their aperture set down channel to trap the fish coming into Bridgwater Bay to feed and are located far out on a spit of shingle. An almost identical version of the sledge was dug from peat beds nearby proving that men were using these in the Bronze Age some 3,000 years ago.

The otter was frequently tempted to chance her arm for a 'freebie' fish but her mother's words and her brother's disappearance, and the sight of grotesque conger eels trapped whilst gorging on the unfortunate netted victims inevitably stopped her. Instead, the large cod and sea bass were collected for Lloyd's the fishmongers of Blackboy Hill In Clifton and the grey mullet were snapped up by the stone to be served as delicacies in West Indian communities throughout the country.

Brendan Sellick, the mud-horse fisherman, sold some of the pout whiting to local cat-lovers but most were taken by a person who owned a large collection of breeding British otters!

The bitch was surrounded by the sounds, smells and sights with which she had become familiar. Not long after she had set up home, the last of the wigeon and teal, the dunlin and the curlew had left and now quarrelsome courting shelduck and piping redshank and oystercatchers were house hunting In the sodden fields or along the shingle ridge.

The only sound that disturbed her when lying up in the absolute still of night-time was the constant hum from the nuclear reactors of the nearby Hinkley Point Power Station. Despite this representing something awesome and man-made, she encountered no other human contact during the early summer. It was for her a period of quiet and essential maturing. What was unknown to her was that there had been a long history of otters residing in this area over many generations. Such otters had always wintered on the foreshore and flats close to Steart Island in Bridgwater Bay, had followed the same stream to its source in the Quantock Hills and thence to high Exmoor to breed. Soon it would seem more than a coincidence that the bitch had again to trace those waters in order to fulfill her adult life.

During her brief early summer sojourn on the coastal marsh close to the Severn Sea she had found no companions. For otters, as elsewhere, were now very scarce. Although she was in many ways at peace with herself, she had begun to experience an inborn urge to find a mate. There was a need to wander even further to fulfil her destiny. With springing grasshoppers and meadow pipits as her nearby neighbours, she enjoyed these transitory days lazily swimming through the drifts of suaeda pods on the summer water and listening In her various couches to the sea wind running like mice through singing summer grasses.

By late summer and now adult, she was on a new territory that included a cluster of fast-moving streams that emerged from the high moor. She was alone in the hills sharing her special area with

14

flocks of black-faced sheep, and with the red deer hinds and their summer-born calves. The buzzards gracefully circling ever upwards on the thermals were her friends, but on the occasions she ventured in broad daylight to enjoy the solitude only appreciated and understood by a wild otter, she found herself being constantly scolded by the marauding resident ravens.

But this boggy and swampy moorland marsh was similar to where in the hills above the River Torridge she had been born. She criss-crossed the area time and again learning to recognise the drains, the bridges and the crossing points of remote farm tracks and lanes. She laid her spraint and thereby defined her territory ready for the possibility of enticing that elusive mate, her roaming dog otter, should he chance to pass through.

She still had as her pals some of the birds whose calls she knew so well from her time spent on the coast, curlew, lapwing, redshank, snipe and golden plover. Blackcaps and sedge warblers were the new birds and sounds as summer migrants In the willow, alder and birch along the streams and amongst the hemp agrimone and willow herb; in the stone walls were wheatears and on the drier open pastures, skylarks. Finally, spellbound, she would watch the ghostly moth-like flight at dawn and dusk, of the resident pair of barn owls over the high meadows drifting like butterflies into the wind as they searched for short-tailed field voles.

Eventually she had chosen an area of dense cover, well drained and on sloping ground. There she created two favourite homes, one naturally underground and within the roots of blackthorn bushes that formed the hedgerow above her and another super daytime couch surrounded by gorse and alder. However, she was surprisingly close to the hill farm which in turn dominated a hamlet of a few houses that encircled an ancient church. The farm catered for holiday visitors with some of the buildings converted into self-catering cottages. She would regularly hear the noise of people and of vehicles, especially the slamming of car doors late at night and the laughter from those coming home from the moorland inn. All these were new noises to which she became very accustomed throughout the late summer.

The farmer had created an artificial trout pond for his guests by damming one of the many local streams. From time to time she had fed there, secretly, coming to the water in the late evening as the last of the swallows and house martins were hawking the aphids and flies. The pond with its source of easy food was an added bounty for the bitch, as was the extensive rabbit warren that sprawled all around in the banks above her holt. Here was another instantly available supply of protein, important for her should she ever become pregnant. There would always be a ready supply of small rabbits whose daytime scurries, however, into the nearby fields also drew the close attention of the resident family of buzzards. Although the rabbits were a bonus, the otter needed to remain unseen in her attempts to catch her prey. Otherwise the sharp-eyed hawks would circle her ever lower overhead and would draw attention to the bitch by their persistent mewing calls. Then there could have been further unwanted investigation from those hiring the cottages.

So the best watchdogs for the otter were firstly the close proximity of yet another family of wrens. They scolded anything passing their territory and which suggested canine, feline or human danger. All was reported by Mr and Mrs Wren. Secondly, the wren's concerns were confirmed or denied by a pair of little owls who regularly brought up their youngsters in the hollow of a nearby oak. The otter also became quite accustomed to the owls' dog-like yapping calls so was quickly aware of the neighbourhood gossip in the local community where she had now established her adult home.

Yet suddenly summer had passed. Although the migrants had followed the warmer weather still the bitch otter waited. She was feeding well, was content, and was constantly marking and redefining her territory. Suddenly one night she heard a distinctive and recognisable call, a whistle, which instinctively she knew was that of a dog otter. She recalled the sound from when her brother would rediscover her after a feeding trip on that first estuary marsh now so long ago.

This dog was, as yet, some distance away on the main stream. However, through the scent trails of the bitch he had soon found his way to the trout pond where she fished most evenings. The dog took advantage of the extensive cover and laid up close to the water. He waited nervously yet excitedly for his first meeting with her.

It was now late October.

Storm's mother had played hard to get. For the best part of two days, at dusk and at dawn, she quietly fed in and around the trout pool. She deliberately marked where she had been by urinating and sprainting. Her inner body responded to the excitement and closeness of the as yet unknown dog otter; he too had left his tell-tale signs which clearly indicated to her that he was anxious to meet. This game of romantic cat and mouse lasted well into the second evening until Storm's mother's desires could be withheld no longer.

She made the first move by breaking cover from the bog cotton grass of the marshy ground which lay behind a dense bed of sedge and reedmace. Slowly she glided effortlessly into the deeper water and with gentle and undulating swimming, so reminiscent of a human's butterfly stroke, hoped secretly to give away her position in the pool. He was late, very late; nearly every other living creature and person was asleep. The 'regulars' were home from the local pub and most of the lights in the cottages were out; the little owls were roosting, the barn owls had hunted and returned and would not be out again until dawn. The only wild noise had been the strident alarm call of one of the resident moorhens. He too had been fast asleep, his head tucked deep into his wing feathers. When Storm's mother had squeezed past him in the reedbed she had frightened him out of his wits.

Fore

Hind

The five widely separated toes may not all show clearly,
but the rounded appearance of print and ball under sole
are visually distinguishable

Suddenly, without warning, the dog otter was alongside her. Storm's mother chittered in surprise. Momentarily they faced one another, their whiskers touching. Although she so wanted to stay close to him, almost in fear she turned away and slipped deeper into the still water. But immediately, and almost simultaneously, he tucked tight in behind her at speed.

For Storm's mother there followed a brief period of instant togetherness so reminiscent of dolphins; they were swimming and diving together almost as one. For ten minutes they carried out this act of getting to know one another. His body brushed against hers and she felt aroused. Suddenly, and she did not resist, the dog had hold of her, the water boiled and together they were one. Minutes later and accompanied by her slight whimperings of delight and encouragement the dog followed her ashore. Quickly but quietly she led him to the blackthorn holt.

They snuggled together and eventually fell asleep, he very closely alongside her with his broad wide head nestled gently in the hollow between her shoulders. Thus, almost interwoven, they passed the night away. Those who lived in the farm, the last of the summer visitors in the holiday barn, the villagers in their homes beyond the church, none were aware of the act of creation that took place that night.

In the early hours she stretched; it was a sunny autumn morning, and only the family of wrens realised their presence as the courting couple took a very brief morning dip before moving to the daytime holt in the dense reed cover.

In deep sleep the couple passed the day, occasionally twitching gently and only stirring to intertwine themselves ever more closely together. All around people, animals and birds went about their everyday business but the two otters were blissfully unaware. It was hours later when the pair of them made their way back to the trout pool; that night their courtship was acted out in a series of rough and tumble games. The water boiled. Storm's mother sometimes chittered in excitement and sometimes in pain as the dog's approaches became more dominant; their intense courtship was less gentle, their mating more direct and thus more fulfilling for both animals.

They stayed together and grew intimate over several days. The weather had been good to them, allowing them to use the daytime reed couch together and although their human neighbours had put the clock forward an hour, marking the end of summer time, the night air was still relatively warm.

Early November heralded the first of a series of wet fronts chasing in from the western Atlantic and their last night together was spent deep in the blackthorn holt. Storm's mother could not understand why but suddenly at first light the dog was gone as quickly as he had arrived. His departure was made easier because it was so swift; a last touch of the whiskers, a final mutual chitter and whimper of affection, just time for her to wish him 'bon voyage' and for him to say 'good luck' as she stayed on the territory she had made her own.

He would wander, perhaps either further upstream and inland roaming higher into wild Exmoor, or he could make his way back eastwards into the less harsh territories of Tarka country. Whichever decision he took, she wondered early that morning whether they would ever meet again. Their coming together had been so brief yet so fulfilling; she thought he was lovely, so handsome, so strong, so wild. She would miss him so much.

She heard his distant and happy whistle; he must have already been far out on the main river. Then she turned and with the rain becoming increasingly heavy and penetrating, she hurried back to the blackthorn holt. Her instincts told her to hesitate well short of the entrance; the wren family were going about their business and with no alarm note forthcoming from them in the next few minutes, she relied on that comforting factor to move in to lie up. There was a final shimmer along the length of her back to discard the rain, a final half-suppressed whimper as she came to terms with the fact that although he was so typical of dog otters, a great wanderer and shy of man, she would now have to stay on her chosen ground and try to do her very best with the fruits of that romantic liaison.

She was young and much around her alien. There would be pitfalls she had never experienced, but above all she must tough it out as only bitch otters can and do. The great adventure of motherhood was just beginning.

Her pregnancy would last sixty-three days, give or take a few hours; a duration no different from the golden retriever and English springer spaniel bitches on the nearby farm.

November was mild and wet which was good news for her. The present litters of rabbits in the nearby warren, born in the last throes of late summer would be mature enough not to be knocked out by the first of the winter frosts. The youngsters would offer a much needed source of protein along with the plentiful supply of

eels in the trout pond, thus allowing her to follow a pre-planned lazy routine of eating and sleeping. Just the lifestyle sought by a pregnant otter!

However it was not long before she had to come to terms with the first problems of motherhood. The bouts of morning sickness were worse than she expected. It was important for her to discharge the greyish saliva-like secretion well away from her nucleus of holts for fear of giving her position away. Within a few days this temporary condition had passed and she was able to return to her regular and trusted routines.

She told no one of her inner happiness, not even the wrens. They might have become so excited that in their noisy gossip all would have been given away. It was imperative too for her to become even more secretive around her existing holts and territory. She remembered how her own mother had explained to her brother and herself just a few weeks after they had been born that it was vital to have a secondary, but special, holt close at hand in case of unforeseen dangers. Now she would take time every few days to establish her all important 'bolt' holt.

December turned much colder and for days at a time westerly winds were replaced by bitingly cold north-easterlies. Every person and every animal was beginning to batten down for winter. Overnight, flocks of redwings and fieldfares descended everywhere around the hamlet. They had originally fled from Scandinavia at the onset of winter and were now moving substantially further south and west, a sure sign that a longer spell of colder weather was imminent. The dippers too had come downstream, vacating the exposed moorland streams for more sheltered waters. Even the wrens were discussing whether to move the short distance to the farm outbuildings. They would be warmer in the nooks and crannies of the machinery now laid up until springtime. Their debate centred around whether the benefit of extra warmth would be offset by the greater danger posed by the predatory farm cats.

The bitch otter naturally wanted the wren family to stay. They were her built-in watchdogs and she could sleep soundly able to rely upon their individual and family-group curiosity towards everything and everybody that would pass by. She spent many of these days upside down fast asleep, knowing that her embryos would be growing quickly. Out and about by necessity only now, she would show no physical and outward sign of her impending motherhood until the very last stages when the cubs would move into position in her uterus.

She continually licked and nuzzled her fur, keeping herself spotlessly clean and finely groomed and it was about mid-December when she suddenly surprised herself. Was she right? Could she now feel three lumps rather than the two she had been gently massaging of late? For the next few days she was tense. Her mother had always given birth to twin cubs, or at least that is what she had been led to understand. The bitch had expected no more than a single cub after her first successful mating. Twins had been a pleasant surprise but triplets that was something else. Her initial excitement was quickly replaced by fear. How would she cope? She was all alone now. Her mother's warmth and closeness were a distant memories and her dog had disappeared as quickly as he had arrived.

What also was worrying her was that two of the fast growing cubs within her womb were much bigger than the third. What did that mean and would it complicate the birth? She had to increasingly feed up every day to satisfy the demand of the triplets in her body, but at the same time she had to be constantly aware of not giving herself away. At dawn one morning she mistook the real size of a young buck rabbit. When she moved quickly in for the kill, he proved much too strong to pull down and his squeals were heard by many other animals and birds. The bitch otter regretted that she may have betrayed her own presence, so for a few days she feasted on the eels in the trout pond. But before long before her body was again craving for the vital protein provided by fresh rabbit meat.

Her expeditions for food became noticeably shorter. She did not take long to spraint and wash and she spent much longer periods of time asleep. In fact days would go by when she was just secreted in deep slumber. Now occasionally she was, frustratingly, disturbed at night by the celebrations of the winter season. The shortest day in the year had past and there were coloured fairy lights twinkling in the windows of the farm.

The kicking of the cubs became more regular within her and one morning she awoke to feel that they had moved into a position to be born. She was both excited and very frightened.

The bitch was sleeping well Christmas Eve, dreaming of her dog and contentedly planning the next day's routine when she was awakened by the sound of church bells and the repeated slamming of car doors. The residents of the local neighbourhood were celebrating Midnight Mass and she could clearly hear the singing of traditonal hymns and carols on the wind. There were more church bells on Christmas Day morning and the day that followed was beautifully quiet. She was able to feed briefly during the late afternoon and in the last of the light. The cubs' movements were stronger and more regular now and the time of their birth was fast approaching.

There was another hard frost that night. But the bitch was snug and warm, covered in the sedges and rushes which she had dragged into the holt over the previous weeks. The family of wrens were up and about earlier than usual, busy scurrying and flicking about under the whitened foliage looking for their breakfast of tiny insects. As always their daily routine reassured her. Regrettably her own sleep had been somewhat disturbed because of her cubs so she tried to settle comfortably for a lie-in with no plans to feed until much later.

Suddenly the wrens were quiet. There was the noise of people and of much heavier doors than usual. What did they mean? They were a new sound. For certain she had never heard them before.

Almost immediately there was the smell and barking of hounds in the cold morning air. Her mother had told her long ago of the fear these large animals caused to the older generations of her family in the 'Land of the Two Rivers': that for many years people had argued against the cruelty of hunting the otter by numbers of hounds with the odds stacked heavily against their prey. This barbaric practice, carried out in the name of sport, had at long last been made illegal.

At all costs she must avoid that anguish now. She was so heavily in labour that she could not have struggled far and if she did manage to elude the threat, the stress and strenuous efforts would cause irreparable damage to the health of her cubs.

Where were her friends the wrens? Normally she could rely on them for the latest information. The bitch otter was fearful now of her safety, for there was bedlam close to the farm from people, hounds and trucks.

Then as suddenly as the noise had started, all became quiet again. Minutes later there was only the odd shout, an occasional shutting of a car door and certainly it appeared the hounds had departed too. She waited and listened closely. The wrens were chattering again amongst themselves and soon she had the news. 'They have come to drag for mink. They're away down river and won't be back till late afternoon.'

She was very disappointed. She had needed briefly to wash and feed. Should she now wait until after dark when everbody had left? She remembered her mother's cautioning to always err on the side of safety. She had fed well in the weeks and days prior to this disturbance and there was no need to take an undue risk at the present time. She slept on with her unborn trio.

Carrying her cubs had taken its toll on the bitch. She was physically tired and what had begun as fitful sleep soon became a deep and relaxed slumber. As she snored heavily she missed receiving her regular news up-date from the wrens. They had watched from afar the return of the vehicles and the people who had celebrated Boxing Day in their traditional manner.

Would it now be a quiet and successful climax to nine weeks of pregnancy for this wild bitch otter? With few problems so far she was looking forward to coping successfully with the most testing time of her life, the birth of her first family,

ONE

"WHY NOT KEEP WILDLIFE AS A HOBBY?"

At precisely the place where I had been instructed, I crawled through the sharp marram grass to the ridge of the dune. There below me were the oyster-catchers I had been trailing for a while now. Further west along the beach and towards the setting sun my employer, the naturalist Philip Wayre, had installed his parabola reflector. He was also hidden in the dunes waiting. His plan was to record the birds' shrill and piping calls against the sound of the gentle waves alternately lapping and receding on the seaward shingle shore. With a fair amount of luck they would eventually pass directly over the equipment.

I made my move. Instantly, a long line of noisy birds rose with rapid wingbeats. All the while they called in increasing intensity, as they hugged the top of the tide directly towards our predetermined spot.

"Well done! a successful recording," was Philip Wayre's enthusiastic remark as I returned to our camp. "We'll continue filming and recording tomorrow morning, so plan to make another early start. You know that I will be leaving ahead of you at lunchtime. In the meantime, would you like to explore the island further? Behind the dunes and on a shingle spit which is obviously above high water mark, you will have a close-up of the sandwich tern colony. It's quite a sight. See you in the morning David, and thanks again. And while you're there look out for the little terns as well," were his final words as he turned away.

Half-an-hour later I was crouched at the foot of the dunes, hiding as best I could behind large clumps of sea holly. Within two or three weeks their mauve corn-flowers would be lost amongst their paler green leaves. The ternery was both a sight and sound of ceaseless commotion; the female birds, either covering clutches of well-set eggs or newly-hatched broods, were continually bickering. They shouted even louder when their

25

respective mates appeared with sand-eels or whitebait after another successful fishing trip. Sometimes the returning birds passed so close overhead that even in the fading light I could glimpse their rich black hoods contrasting with their yellow-tipped pale bills. But in all the toing and froing there were none of the less common and elusive little terns. Maybe I would catch up with those tomorrow, I thought to myself, as I went to move quietly away.

Then, suddenly, there was a whistle, distant but brief and abrupt. I froze, and the hairs rose on the back of my neck. It was certainly not man-made, and in any case there was no-one else on the island. I desperately wanted the terns to be silent.

I decided to wait, determined to hear that sound again. Darkness, or at least twilight, fell slowly in mid-summer. I learned that tern colonies are never silent, even at night, except when a moment of unrest circulates through the crowds of nesting birds. It must have been a good hour later and at just such a moment, when I definitely heard whistles again, but this time they were a less agitated noise.

I reflected on the day and the night. Much earlier that morning I had accompanied Ted Eales, boatman and warden to Scolt Head Island, from the quay at Brancaster Staithe. I had spent the late afternoon picking, and then washing, a large bucketful of samphire grass, and later we would cook it, seasoned and in butter to eat as a starter before our barbecue; we had successfully recorded the oyster-catchers against a background of a mid-summer North Sea shore, and I had experienced my first tern colony. Finally there were those two mysterious, but different, whistles; all these events because of a letter received a few months previously.

I slid into my sleeping bag, and that night I had no idea whatsoever of the future significance for me of the north Norfolk coastal marshes. For the moment I had identified for the first time, two distinctive sounds that in later years, I was to come to understand well. The original whistle had been made no doubt, by a bitch otter on her territory, as she fended off an attempted coupling by a passing dog otter.

Their encounter had up to that moment been all too brief, and his attempt to establish his dominance, far too hasty. However, the second and later call had almost certainly reflected quieter and deeper affection, as bitch and dog parted company, their short-lived but passionate liaison having been strongly consummated.

26

You can stay with Gabrielle Bordewich and Ian Anderson
near Torrin, close to Loch Slapin on the Isle of Skye and
see wild otters regularly.
Telephone or Fax 01471 822734 for further details.

"I gather that Peter Scott suggests you write to Philip Wayre who lives in Norfolk, to see if he will offer you employment," my father had announced across the breakfast room table.

"So I'm not wanted at Slimbridge then," I replied, slightly taken aback by the content of the letter. On my father's advice, I had previously written to Peter Scott, the director of the Wildfowl Trust at Slimbridge in Gloucestershire, to see if there was the possibility of my working with his world famous collection of ducks, geese and swans. Eighteen months later I would be leaving Bristol where I had been at school at Clifton College, in order to read Geography for three years at Pembroke College, Cambridge.

"He doesn't exactly say that, does he?" Dad continued as he re-read the letter. "He points out that since you have been involved for a long time now at the Trust both as a visitor and particularly as a junior member, it could well be for the best to pursue your interests much further afield. He stresses that you would still be involved in similar work. I must say it seems a sensible idea to me, taking you away from home, opening up fresh horizons, and giving you the opportunity of meeting new companions with similar interests."

I proceeded with my breakfast, my mind slowly adjusting from the convenient scenario which I had planned for some time now. Indeed at that moment I was thinking of Slimbridge, or the New Grounds as they were appropriately named, meadows of reclaimed land lying immediately behind the sea-wall of the River Severn. I recalled the hours of happy times I had already spent there and the staff who had befriended me as a youngster, Tommy and Diana Johnstone, Mike Garside and especially Dougie Eccleston, all of whom were to remain close friends in later years.

I had first visited in the winter of 1950 on the advice of my paternal grandmother, whose imagination had been fired after hearing a live outside radio broadcast conducted by Scott from a hide where it was possible to overlook the large flocks of grazing geese and ducks, Russian white-fronted geese and wigeon. Every autumn thousands of wildfowl wintered close to the Dumbles, the water meadows and saltings lying above the usual high water-mark and which were and still are, summer grazed by flocks of sheep. My father had bought me a copy of one of Scott's early publications 'Evening Chorus', on that first occasion. On subsequent visits, I had been introduced to amongst others, Konrad Lorenz, the author of 'King Solomon's Ring', as he was standing thigh deep in the water with Scott at the four o'clock feeding time in the Big Pen. On Boxing Day morning one year, when part of my Christmas treat was yet another trip to enjoy the magic of the birds, I had met Field Marshal the Viscount Alanbrooke, then a Life President of the Trust.

During my teenage years I had entered into correspondence with Peter Scott, writing to him about my different wildlife experiences; I had suggested a Junior Club membership, and, after his daughter Nicola, had joined as the first 'outside' Gosling member. Already I was keeping several of my favourite native ducks and geese at home in the back garden. So yes, at that moment, Slimbridge did seem the obvious work experience.

I was still lost in my thoughts when my father's voice interrupted me as he left to go downstairs to start another day's work in the drawing offices of his architect's practice.

"Perhaps the more serious aspect of Scott's letter, and of which you should take more heed, is his warning to keep wildlife simply as a hobby, and to earn your living elsewhere."

"Do we need to have that discussion right now?" I snapped and in retrospect, rather unfairly. "After all, any experience will only last for the next eighteen months or so before I go up to Cambridge."

"I realise that, but take time whenever you can to think long and hard about other options and opportunities," he added calmly. "In the meantime however, will you draft a letter of introduction to this fellow in Norfolk?"

I did not reply, but as I gathered my ideas I felt that I was in some way already acquainted with Philip Wayre. Just days before Christmas 1957 I had stood in the darkness on platform 3 at Bristol Temple Meads station excitedly awaiting the London-Penzance express. On its arrival I had hurriedly made my way to the parcels van at the rear of the train, and after some delay, caused by the guard searching through a mountain of Christmas parcels destined for the West Country, I was given a box clearly but variously labelled, 'Livestock', 'This side up', 'Handle with care'. Hurriedly I made my way back to the departure gate through the steam and the crowds of passengers departing against a background of slamming carriage doors. The guards were quickly making the express ready for the next stage of its journey to Exeter, Plymouth and beyond. But I was clutching very tightly the box containing my first pair of tufted ducks. They had been hand-reared in the collection of Philip Wayre, of Hawks Hill, Great Witchingham, Norfolk, and had been purchased for £7 out of my savings. Little did I realise in our family breakfast room that morning, immediately after the initial disappointing news from Peter Scott, that Philip Wayre's positive reply to the letter I was about to write was to alter the whole course of my life. So now north Norfolk was to shortly become a reality, and beyond that, Cambridge still beckoned.

In early June 1967, I was standing on a grassy terraced bank overlooking a pool, landscaped with a pebble beach and sea boulders, in my wildlife park in Bristol. Next to me and about to officially open the grounds to the general public was Peter Scott. Alongside him was another outstanding naturalist of this century, his close friend Ronald Lockley. Lockley's eyes were wandering towards a trio of his beloved Atlantic grey seals; they were eight

or nine months old; they had been rescued when pups of less than three weeks of age and still covered in long white hair; they had all been victims of gales in the previous autumn and I had subsequently hand-reared them.

At the same time and not far away in another pool, which was similarly fed by the waters of the River Trym, my first bitch otter played in the early evening light. Small but separated groups of young deer roamed in the wooded valley; red deer from the 'Warnham' herd in Sussex, true menil fallow deer from the Earl of Leicester's estate at Holkham Hall in north Norfolk; always shyer and so often hard to pick out amongst the denser vegetation by the water's edge were delicate Chinese water deer from the Showering Estates at Shepton Mallet in Somerset. Other exhibits that were ready for the forthcoming visitors included hand-reared foxes and badgers, grey and red squirrels and various species of hawks and owls. It was planned that children would be able to ride the Shetland and Dartmoor ponies, and also be able to hand-feed the bottle-reared Jacobs and Soay sheep. Finally pheasants, resplendent goldens, silvers, and lady amhersts, and grey and red-legged partridges mingled both with the deer and amongst my now comprehensive collection of native wildfowl.

Thus I had begun to create my very own wildlife park. It was to specialise in the displaying of native British wildlife, and the wide ranging collection already there for the guests to share and enjoy with my close personal friends, and with the local press and television reporters that June evening, was the fruition of two years very hard work and preparation since leaving Cambridge.

The collection was greatly expanded over the next decade. The theme throughout was 'conservation through education', and many people still remember today the impact of the park and the reputation it carried throughout the Westcountry and beyond. With my staff, I took selected hand-reared animals and birds into classrooms throughout the winter months; the schools then visited in the spring and summer terms to complete the experience. In turn, their parents came during the summer holidays to share their youngsters' enthusiasm and memories.

I forged strong links with both television channels in Bristol.

Most of my work with the independent company Television Wales and West, eventually to become Harlech Television, was to contribute to magazine programmes and to news stories concerning the then current conservation issues of the day. The presence in the studio of the species under question added greatly to the impact on the viewer. Under the directorship of producer Sebastian Robinson, a half-hour documentary entitled 'Safari in the City' was commissioned. It was recognition, I believe, of what an urban-based wildlife park could offer, and was already giving the half million or so residents of the Bristol-Bath conurbation.

Similarly, I also had the privilege of adding to some of the early ground-breaking wildlife series which bore all the hallmarks of the now world-renowned BBC Natural History Unit. This had been founded in Whiteladies Road in Clifton, Bristol, some ten years or so previously in 1957 by Desmond Hawkins, and the studios were not three miles distant from Westbury-on-Trym, and the park. I can recall on many occasions during the day-long rehearsals for the live presentations of the early series of 'Animal Magic', enjoying the broadcasting technique of the irresistible Johnny Morris, under the guidance of producers Doug Thomas and George Inger. Eventually, sadly, there had to be a replacement programme. But by then I wonder how many hundreds of thousands of youngsters had become hooked on the 'world natural'.

Then I remember providing barn owls and triplet otter cubs for 'Wildtrack' with Tony Soper, and a female snowy owl for the

31

'Really Wild Show' and Chris Packham. Handling a hand-tame female European eagle owl whilst dressed as a medieval rook-catcher for John Sparks' 'Discovery of Animal Behaviour' series, and filmed on location in Dorset by Hugh Miles was challenging too. Equally demanding many years later was filming with Storm over a period of twelve days for the Unit's prestigious 'Wildlife on One' series. Produced by Martha Holmes and directed on location by Sarah Byatt, 'Otters, the Truth', was the culmination of over two years in the planning and making. I spent many hours with Storm and the film crew around the peat moors, bogs and streams of north Cornwall, establishing the necessary tight shots for editing into the final version that was initially shown, and recently repeated, on prime-time BBC1 television.

So four hours filming and only one overnight stay with Storm in September '98, completed a sequence for Andrew Cooper's 'The Farm That Time Forgot'. It was again commissioned by the Natural History Unit and brings my involvement with Storm and with the various media almost up to date. Even after all their setbacks, otters still frequent the River Erme and its adjacent tributaries, as they did when H.G. and Elaine Hurrell watched their waters at the time of having their own otters, Topsy and Turvy, over forty years ago. The film will feature the organically cultivated meadows of a south Devon river valley, and the rich wildlife still thriving around the farm, its outbuildings and in the nearby woodlands and streams.

During an early reconnaissance trip Andrew had discovered the spraint of wild otters in a place where Storm could also be safely released. Her subsequent lengthy exploration of a gravelly beach confirmed the presence of more than one of her wild cousins. Warwick Sloss, our ever patient cameraman for 'Otters the Truth' who filmed Storm on the remote moorland of north Cornwall would, I guess, have gladly swapped places with Mark Payne-Gill as in south Devon, Storm was so active for the required period of filming.

In the late seventies, the demands for my lecture programme 'Wildlife Face to Face', were such that when eventually I was able to place most of my collection, I closed my park and concentrated on my educational work. However, other than those individual exhibits that I needed, I was determined to keep my already unique but private collection of British otters. In any case, I was hoping to breed further otter cubs, and indeed on a regular basis and in sufficient numbers to contribute to a remarkable project. Not only were my bitches breeding successfully but their cubbing was ongoing over successive years. Many of the offspring were then donated to Philip and Jeanne Wayre's Otter Trust, at Earsham in Suffolk.

The Trust was covering hitherto unexplored ground as with the cooperation of the Nature Conservancy Council, now English Nature, the Wayre's embarked upon a release programme to the wild of captive-bred animals. Presently over one hundred unrelated individuals have been released into the watersheds of predominantly lowland rivers, mostly in eastern England. Several of my youngsters have contributed to that unparalleled success.

So not surprisingly the world of the British otter, and in particular, but sadly, its dramatic decline, has dominated my thoughts for the past twenty years. Within the serious content of my lectures they were always, and still are, the perfect example to illustrate how we have become increasingly intolerant and unworthy of the natural environment around us. Inevitably my work, as the breeding successes continued, drove me even further into attempting to make my own personal and individual contribution to their recovery. Therefore I continue to tell others about the world of these fantastic creatures, which are so wild and so rare, yet whose private and personal lives are still so threatened. I remind younger people about the plight of otters and also, crucially, about the demise of the places where those otters live in their wetland habitats, both freshwater and marine.

The impetus to that programme of dedication and effort was polarised when my wife Helen answered the telephone enquiry from the remote Quantock Hills with the words, 'are you sure it's not a mink?'

The helpless wild otter cub that was to mature into the redoubtable and remarkable Storm, was about to join our family, and therefore her impact on countless other people was about to begin. Her contribution to otter and wetland conservation remains immeasurable.

Through the eyes and mind of one particular otter Storm, the bitch cub of a wild adult female, and through the story of the decline of her wild relatives in these islands, *Stormforce* is my attempt to relate to the reader what I believe is the purpose of

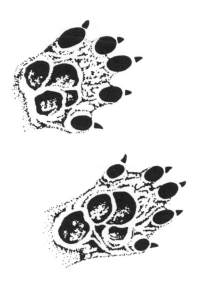

*You can see Pebble and Ripple and their current offspring
at the Tamar Otter Sanctuary which is situated at
North Petherwin, five miles NW of Launceston off the
B3254 road to Bude, North Cornwall. Telephone 01566 785646.*

Storm's life, given her very special circumstances. This is simply summarised by the words of the title of the forthcoming final chapter, 'You do take my life when you do take the means whereby I live.' Or put another way, 'It's the quality of life that counts, and not always the quantity of material gains squeezed out of life at every opportunity.' Surely, surely down deep inside us, we already know the meaning and ultimate consequences of those few words. We are already fully aware that Planet Earth has limited and finite resources. So what kind of world do we want, and what are the prospects we are currently leaving for our youngsters and for the world natural?

Nearly fifty years ago one of Peter Scott's radio broadcasts led me to Slimbridge. Later his personal letter suggested I must go to Norfolk where I was to hear the calls of my first wild otters. I spent my wildlife park years displaying animals and birds, and through them I had the means to communicate to others my concern for the environment. The wildlife park was also responsible for bringing, most wonderfully, both my wife Helen and subsequently Olivia into my life. Finally the arrival of the wild otter Storm, after over twenty-five years of keeping and breeding otters for release, seems to have tied many loose ends together. My presentations with her have reminded me what my early lecturing days had taught me – how vital it is to share the evolution and innate beauty of wild animals with other people. I hope that those, who through their circumstances cannot live close to one of the world's most romantic and exciting creatures, will be persuaded to do something very positive for the future of otters everywhere. By their action they will have simultaneously contributed both to their own and their children's environments: and so in turn, will have helped their children's children too.

The message from Stormforce is as simple as that, and I trust you will embrace it.

> 'In today's world of high consumption and over-population, it is essential to keep youngsters in touch with the earth: its changing seasons, its natural rhythms, its beauty and its mysteries. In fact, nothing will suffice short of teaching youngsters to love nature, ...and to love life.'
>
> Joseph Cornell, *Sharing Nature with Children.*

TWO

"THINK OF A TITLE"

It was a damp and cold morning and there was an eerie atmosphere around; the low cloud, drifting in from the western Atlantic, was partially blanketing the grotesque granite outcrops of the nearby Rosewall Hill skyline.

"Is that your birthday card from Olivia?" I enquired as I entered Storm's enclosure.

"Yes, I heard Olivia earlier; she was trying to be very quiet in order not to disturb me; you know how much I love my lie-ins," responded Storm sleepily. "I believe Olivia was attempting to attach her card to my door, but she was having great difficulty pushing the drawing pins into the hard wood. She became rather frustrated."

"I don't doubt it," I interrupted, thinking of our daughter's usual impatience.

"But eventually she fastened it safely. The card is very pretty, isn't it? She designed it on her computer, with lovely blue and purple colours. I especially like the fish, and seal, and dolphin characters drawn against that background; I think I am meant to be swimming with them."

I allowed Storm time to stretch and roll, and to rub herself in her favourite towel. Half upside down she yawned very fully and deliberately. Even in the half-light I could see the fuchsia pink colour of the roof of her mouth; then there was one very rapid burst of scratching with her right paw just behind her right ear before she finally curled up even more tightly within herself. She was content, her head and shoulders were lying almost at right angles to the main trunk of her body and forelegs, with her sleek and dark brown upper body contrasting vividly against the pale blue of her towel and the golden yellow of the wheat straw beneath her.

"Do you remember, Storm, your mother telling you that the

weather was bad the night she gave birth? No matter wherever you are in the Westcountry at this time of winter, it always seems to be very wet and very windy, and definitely colder than a few years back. Early this morning the exposed moors hereabouts and high on Exmoor where you were born will almost certainly be shrouded in the same enveloping mists."

"Yes, it had rained for days, and I remember mum telling us she was frightened in case the rising river water might threaten to flood the holt. She had two homes for us but this was her first choice. Other than that problem my brothers and I were as safe as houses in there."

"Well anyway," I interrupted, "have a lovely time today, just you enjoy yourself. Olivia is off to a school-friend's Christmas party. She's not far away in Towednack. I will feed you later this afternoon after Helen and I have brought her home. When she has gone to bed tonight, I will come as usual and spend some more time with you. Perhaps we can sit up together and I will go through the plans I have been making for the year ahead.

"That would be nice" murmured Storm.

With that I ran my fingers down the nape of her neck and spine in just the same way as I do when spending time with our English springer spaniel. And just like Sasha, Storm, if it were at all possible, would curl herself up even more tightly, and would turn herself even more inside out and upside down! As on so many occasions previously I left her snoring; a last glance and I could clearly see the bright white patch on the lower side of her upper right lip; all British otters have varying but distinctive blotches, streaks, or patterns of white of different shape and size, on the lips or on the throat, or on both, all of which serve to distinguish them one from another. These markings also allow them to identify parents, mates or siblings at close range. Of course, this colour patterning is no different from the varying amount or shape of black to be found on the yellow bills of individual Bewick's swans and which in turn serves as a means of identification between adult birds.

Storm, born to her wild mother five years ago today, had distinctive markings which therefore made her separate from every other wild British otter.

As I had promised her earlier, I returned to sit with Storm much later that same night. Olivia had returned from her party highly excited and as always had needed to describe everything that had happened in great detail to Helen and myself. Now I had left her fast asleep. Meanwhile, Storm had eaten her main meal of the day, her supper, and was now busily exploring for the right place in my lap in which to flop. Simultaneously, I was running my fingers in a circular fashion over the pads on her forefeet and just occasionally I would slip one finger very gently in between the pads. This would obviously tickle her and most times she would not object, but would continue to burrow her head searching for that ideal position. Sometimes, and for no apparent reason, she would chitter rather aggressively in annoyance. Then I knew from previous experience the best policy was to leave that particular line of play alone for a while. However on the great majority of occasions she clearly enjoyed the sensation, and again tonight Storm continued to twist and rub herself for some time before finally and contentedly settling down. Outside it was still raining heavily.

"At the moment there is no more filming booked," I began, "but we are already due to return to Wales on at least three occasions next year, including the Royal Welsh Show again. However, the first appointment is at Christs College Brecon, for Brecknock Wildlife Trust's annual lecture. That promises to be a very good occasion with a committed and enthusiastic audience."

This was also the first night that I saw Storm slip back into the routine to which she had previously become accustomed. After nearly five years with us in Somerset, she had been in the far west of Cornwall, where as a family we had come to live, for no more than a fortnight. The change for her, as with the house move for us, had been profound. I knew that she had been very upset by a recent event, and judging by her constant recalling of that episode every night since her arrival, I understood that her sadness would remain for a while longer yet.

Sure enough again tonight, although I had initially tried to distract her mind by discussing our next planned work together, it was not long before the same anxieties resurfaced.

"You were with Cider, weren't you, on that night when I heard him talking about how families of people may come and go from an area but that generations of otters will endure."

"Don't worry Storm," I reassured her, "I was there. Previously Cider had suffered a worrying setback in his health, the equivalent of a severe heart attack. He had done well to survive that at all. But he knew, and I knew, that sadly his days with us were finally numbered. So I used to sit and listen to him as he reminisced: old people do the same, they recall happy times, holidays when the sun shone and memorable occasions with grandchildren. They recall time spent as a child and for Cider that included being successfully hand-reared from a tiny cub along with his brother Perry after their mother's milk had suddenly failed. I had fetched him from the Otter Trust in Suffolk and brought him to Somerset to join our family group. Against my better judgement, I had immediately placed him with a bitch called Rosie on his first night of arrival, giving them no time, as I should have done, to become accustomed to each other. Unbelievably they were immediately fondly together and Rosie gave birth to a male cub within sixty-seven days of his arrivial. My risky gamble had worked!"

"Is my friend Blackthorn that dog cub?" Storm was already looking much happier.

"Yes, his father Cider was just a gentle giant. Cider went on to sire many more cubs over the following years through his constant companion, a bitch I had bred, called Rowan. In turn, I paired her sister Houdini with yet another of my home-bred dog otters. He was called Fred!"

"How many cubs did Rowan bring up?" interrupted Storm.

"Oh, I would need to look up the exact details in my records but I can remember for sure that between them both they were well into double figures, fifteen at least."

Storm gasped. "Cider must have kept his prowess well to himself."

"Yes, Rowan always gave birth to twins or triplets by Cider," I continued, "but Houdini only ever had a single cub by Fred. But she was much wilder than her sister, much more aggressive towards me, so I could never accurately check her immediately after she had given birth as I could with Rowan. She could well have been giving birth to twins. But whatever, only one cub eventually showed at about two months of age. Something else that would interest you, too, was that these twin sisters always gave birth roundabout the third week of April. I can definitely remember April 24th being a key date. They always seemed to cub within seventy-two hours of one another. One spring it all went wrong; I think both must have shared a strange experience together"

"Are you saying that both Rowan and Houdini were similarly affected?"

"Yes. Rowan had triplet cubs prematurely which Helen and I

failed to save even though we attempted to revive them using the gentle heat of a hairdryer. No squeaking either came from Houdini's holt. In fact, she never really went to ground. So knowing that just after giving birth bitch otters can mate immediately, I put both dogs to them again. Would you believe it? Rowan and Houdini both had litters again by the end of June and within a couple of days of each other."

"Amazing," said Storm.

"Yes it was, but towards the end of her breeding cycle Houdini brought up litters of twins twice. She must have been nine or ten by then, but fine cubs they all were. By now she was running with Blackthorn. Twin bitches on her last cubbing, I remember them well, as big as some dog cubs that Houdini had previously reared, but this time of course taking after their father Blackthorn. Helen and I took both of them to the Otter Trust."

"Cider used to tell me what happened at the Trust's headquarters in Bungay."

"Yes Cider knew that we had also taken some of his offspring by Rowan to Suffolk in order to contribute to the trios of otters being released into the wild, and to introduce new blood lines into their ongoing breeding programme. So all in all he was very content in his later years, thrilled that sons and daughters of his were probably already breeding on some secluded river bank. That means," I concluded, "that his grandchildren will now be repopulating some of the remote haunts from where wild otters have sadly disappeared."

"Then he had me to look after as well," said Storm excitedly, "and I knew he enjoyed doing that because he used to tell me so, frequently."

"Yes, he was very fond of you; you're arrival gave him an unexpected but extra-special relationship. He used his lifelong experiences to explain everything that was going on around you, all those little 'ottery' things that your mother would have spelt out for you. In turn, he loved you telling him about your exploits with your wild mother."

"I told you, didn't I," said Storm with an obvious tinge of sadness back in her voice again, "that recently he was continually talking about how he was shortly going to meet old friends again and especially his mother whom he hadn't known for very long."

"That was exactly the reason why he had such an attachment and understanding for you, because both of you had lost your mothers so early in life.

41

Cider was so very typical of all our otters that I have come to know so well over the last thirty years. Wild otters are creatures that have been around for many tens of thousands of years, and it seems they are blessed with a unique aura of mystery about them, surrounded by a timelessness that is so hard to define. Maybe it is because most of them live in remote and wild places and are in tune with the time clocks of season and tide rather than the hour by hour clock by which most of us live our daily lives."

"He didn't seem to be that old when I used to talk to him, I wish I still had him for company."

"Luckily his mind was still very active in later life, his reasoning and thoughts were remarkably clear but his body was going into sharp decline. He knew the end was near but, for instance, he would talk to me quite excitedly about the news you had brought to him from Cornwall and the Tamar Otter Sanctuary where you had stayed, about his son Blackthorn, and his grand-daughters Ripple and Pebble. He had been cheered up no end by becoming a grandfather yet again, this time to triplets of course."

"But I am all on my own now. Because he lived next door to me, it was Cider I talked to whenever you were away."

"Well, I still have to continue with that conservation work now. It is vital for otters everywhere and you must help me; we both know that Cider would have wanted that for all his many pals, and particularly from you Storm."

"He used to tell me I was a special otter you know, and that because of my wild background, I would achieve much for otters everywhere if I continued going to lectures and presentations with you."

"Well there you are then. Shall we go on doing just that for Cider, and for all the wild otters wherever they may be tonight throughout the British Isles?" I concluded.

"Yes, that would be good, that would make me very happy."

Storm looked much brighter than for some time, the sadness I had detected earlier had now passed, so I proceeded to outline the coming year to her. A return to the Royal Welsh Show, a special lecture in Llandindrod Wells, there was a distinct possibility of going to the Devon County Show, and I was tempted to explore one or two other possibilities including the Royal Cornwall Show to be held at Wadebridge in June. But first and foremost was combining again with Geoff Liles and his 'Otters in

Wales' project. We were to meet up in Brecon for the annual lecture of Brecknock Wildlife Trust. Combining with Storm, he and I had already worked successfully together in Builth Wells for the 1996 Royal Welsh Show with the cooperation of the Welsh Environment Agency and Welsh Water, promoting all that needed to be urgently done in order to now sustain the encouraging and continual recovery of otters throughout wild Wales.

"Try and put Cider's passing behind you," I continued. "It really was a blessing in disguise that eventually he died so peacefully. He was completely at one with himself; he couldn't have been happier than with Helen, Olivia and yourself in his latter years when he was an ageing old boy. Storm, he was fourteen plus when he went on," I said quite determinedly, "So, look upon yourself as an ambassador for otters everywhere, and just treasure your memories of Cider, always."

My words had the desired effect.

"Tell me about your plans for Brecon," replied Storm .

It was quite late when finally Storm made her way into her den for the rest of the night. I rearranged her remaining food, repositioned her towels, and before I had finally locked up, I could

hear her gentle snoring. I decided not to awaken her again but, very quietly, stayed close to her.

It was in the absolute still and quiet of the winter night and because of the sadness which, like Storm, I similarly felt for dear old Cider, that I paused and reflected on why I had come to be living in west Cornwall. Asleep close by were my lovely wife Helen and our enchanting daughter Olivia, now just ten years of age. At moments like these my thoughts inevitably wandered briefly to the successive events and the different people who had shaped my individual career within the wildlife conservation movement.

Above all, I fondly remembered the inspirational friendship of the late Sir Peter Scott, freely given to me from an early age. Another gentle and gifted naturalist in exactly the same mould as Scott, is Ronald Lockley. His original research into the seabird colonies on the enchanting islands of Skomer and Skokholm which lie off the Pembrokeshire coast, made marvellous reading when I was young. Before his untimely death, Gavin Maxwell's writings were equally thought provoking in a very different way. Sadly we never met but at least we were corresponding. I would never have believed that as his all time best selling story of otters, 'Ring of Bright Water', was being launched in 1967, I was already deeply involved with the creature that still dominates my everyday thoughts on wildlife.

More practically, a very formative time spent in Norfolk immediately after leaving Clifton College in Bristol, and before going up to Pembroke College Cambridge to read Geography eighteen months later, was to prove much more decisive than I first imagined. I worked for the charismatic Philip Wayre, a man with an intense determination to complete a particular task as well as possible. This would range from rearing a brood of extremely rare ducklings or pheasant chicks with absolutely no losses, to the completing of outstanding wildlife films, accurate to the very last detail, such as 'Wind in the Reeds' and 'Wind on the Heath'.

Philip lives with his wife Jeanne in Suffolk, close to the Waveney marshes and water-meadows. He had the dream, and together they are the driving force behind the Otter Trust who have now released over one hundred British otter cubs back into the wild. By meeting at the same time all the criteria set down by English Nature, they or rather the Trust, can claim quite realistically to be responsible for the recovery of the otter in the lowland counties of East Anglia. The rivers Wensum and Yare, the

Stiffkey marshes, the Glaven water meadows and the reed-fringed waters of the more remote fenlands and broads are now all places where, at long last, the high-pitched calls of mating otters can be heard again across the waters.

But tonight my mind drifted to the planning for Brecon. This time with Geoff Lilles it would be a much more formal occasion; there would be the need to include references to the work of the well known naturalists associated with the world of otters and the wetlands where they live. I would need to prepare additional flash-cards to ensure that I was up-to-date with my text. I recollected that I had recently filed a cutting about the late Jacques Cousteau, another most influential expert on the world wildlife conservation stage who like Gavin Maxwell, I was sadly never to meet. Cousteau was not only concerned with the aquatic living world. As Peter Scott did not just restrict himself to fighting the disappearance of the world's wetlands where his cherished wildfowl lived, Cousteau when confronting say the demise of whales, realised that many of the problems they faced also applied directly to the future survival of mankind itself. On Cousteau's office wall at his Paris headquarters was a most relevant quotation; 'happiness for a dolphin is simply to exist, for a man it is to know and wonder'. At the Brecon lecture there would be a good percentage of younger people in the audience; I would ask them to substitute otter for dolphin.

It is at moments like this, alone with my thoughts, and perhaps as tonight, planning some of the details of my next public presentation, that I am again quickly aware of the pleasure I can give to others after my thirty years with these wonderful creatures, and even more so when working with the exceptional Storm herself. There is no substitute to witnessing the delight within an audience as you catch the sense of wonder reflected in young peoples' faces. Suddenly you know you can be responsible, you are responsible, for influencing young minds for the greater good. With their plight in mind and by stressing that otters are flying red danger signals for the future, I can stress that *we* as parents, and *they* critically as the next generation, must work for a world where it is the quality of life that really counts, and not the quantity of material gains to be squeezed out of life at every opportunity.

The driving misty rain had quite dampened me by the time I quietly slipped away to bed.

British Otters are on display at Vale House Farm, The Otter Trust's North Pennines Reserve which is situated near Bowes, County Durham, on the south side of the main A66 Scotch Corner to Penrith road. Telephone 01833 628339.

"Excuse me Mr Chaffe," the lady chairperson of the meeting had interrupted me politely. "It's now a quarter to ten and much as we would like to hear more from you, and to continue watching Storm, many of our members and guests have lengthy journeys home, and I still have to close the meeting."

I asked for a few moments more to conclude. Towards the end of my presentation I had been handling Storm near to the front rows of the audience, and they had been spellbound to be so close to a live British otter. But now Storm was back within the confines of her temporary enclosure with its tank and travelling crate, and its artificial furniture of straw bales, chairs and towels. Within minutes the official business of the meeting had been completed, and many of the two hundred plus audience were swarming in as close as possible to the taped safety barrier to obtain one final and close-up view of Storm. By this late hour she was now visibly and rapidly tiring before them. I knew Roger Dale, my assistant from Cornwall for this lecture, would keep a close eye on affairs. One of several criteria laid down by English Nature, and to be met at all times before lecturing 'live' with Storm is that I am always accompanied by an assistant.

I stepped aside, instinctively knowing that the evening had been a great success. The sweat was literally running off my body beneath the heavyweight fisherman's smock which I always wear when working with a wet otter. Absorbed by the audience's excited reaction, I watched with a feeling of great satisfaction, noting their animated conversations and expressions of pleasure.

'She's so pretty, quite beautiful in fact.....'

'Did you see her rubbing herself on top of the straw bale? You can quite imagine them doing just that in some reedbed or other.....'

'She was so supple when swimming, they obviously do it just for fun as well, don't they.....''

'She really went for that fellow helping when he took the liberty of straightening one of her towels......'

Comments were coming thick and fast, and yes, I did think at that moment in time that really I was very privileged to be earning my living doing what no-one else can, or is allowed to do with a live British otter, to be lecturing on the problems facing one of the world's most endangered yet romantic of species. In Storm's case, I was under licence from English Nature, and the only person in the United Kingdom with an exemption for a British otter held in a private collection to be used both for scientific and educational purposes, and also for commercial gain. I was on a high, my adrenalin had been running strongly for some time. I felt absolutely no tiredness, and I could have answered questions on my subject for another two hours. However for the moment Storm was now the overwhelming attraction for our guests during their precious final minutes in her company. No need now for yet another catalogue of the more disappointing and disturbing facts about the decline of otters. People were pushing past one another politely and discreetly, but always trying to squeeze in ever closer to her. Storm, for her sake, was as a teenage girl, like my lovely Helen when we first met all those years ago, aware of her sensuality, but showing it only occasionally whilst tantalisingly retaining most of her femininity for more private and personal occasions.

The audience certainly did not realise that Storm was watching them even more closely than they were watching her. The college sixth former who was in charge of the arrangements for the lecture theatre and its accompanying lighting and who before the talk had commenced, had also so ably organised the exact positioning of the spotlights to enhance my handling of Storm, had now returned. The ultra-bright light of ten minutes previously was quickly replaced by a starkly contrasting dimness but even in the now half-light and by standing behind and above the audience in the theatre, I could still glimpse the whites of Storm's eyes. She was constantly observing the ranks of individuals, including the many happy and noisy youngsters, whilst at the same time watching the ever-changing situation around her.

I relaxed a little and began to think about the next stage of the long day. Shortly Roger and I would have to dismantle the enclosure and recrate Storm. Then there was the short journey to stay overnight on the hill farm belonging to Gareth and Jane Jones high above Llangorse Lake in the Black Mountains. Much indeed had already happened that day from my very early start in west Cornwall. I remember wondering at first light why it always seemed to rain very heavily whenever Storm and I had an important function to complete together, and when such long distances were involved. I had diverted from my way north on the A30 to collect Roger Dale from his home close to the Tamar Otter Sanctuary. Storm knew him well through other work we had already completed together. But it had then taken a further four hours travelling in quite appalling weather conditions until we reached our venue at Christs College, Brecon. The visibility was so poor that after continuing over the Avon Bridge and past the newly constructed interchange linking the M5 to the second and more southerly Severn crossing, that inadvertently I became muddled within the host of new motorway signs. So instead of finding myself heading into Wales, via the first and old Severn bridge in order to connect to the hill road through Trelleck and Raglan, a route I knew well and had used many times previously to Brecon and beyond to west and mid Wales, there we were heading back south west to the new bridge again! This was very frustrating and unnecessary on such a poor day. We were late for our hosts, and the mistake had proven an anxious and lengthy addition to our journey; just what was not needed before setting up Storm to go 'live'. The fish and chip supper kindly provided was enjoyable and much needed, but eaten with an ever watchful eye on the clock, and our thoughts much on the important and imminent occasion.

It had been previously agreed that Geoff Liles of 'Otters in Wales' would commence the evening with a general introduction and a slide presentation. We hoped and planned that Storm would become 'active' after Geoff had completed his contribution, with the success of the 'show' really depending upon Storm acting as if on cue. I had worked with her on enough previous occasions to know realistically, but frustratingly with most wild creatures under artificial conditions, that completely unforeseen noises and smells, along with the excited buzz of the expectant strangers in a nearby audience, could cause any best laid plans to come unstuck. To be fair Storm had never let me down; just once she had resisted cooperating at my beckoning. But I well remember special mitigating circumstances on her part before that function. My worry was that there would always be a first occasion, and I was fearful of Storm and I disappointing an enthusiastic audience full of eager anticipation from being able to watch a British otter at close quarters. Yet true to form, Storm had excelled herself again that night, and at that moment in time I was an extremely happy and contented person.

The Joneses shared with us the true hospitality of the Welsh hill-farmer. Supper was both wholesome and very plentiful, the warmth and also the subtle flavours of the home-made vegetable broth were particularly enjoyable on a night when the temperatures outside had suddenly dropped like a stone. The remote buildings, nestling tight into the hillside at some fifteen hundred feet, are surrounded by the last of the rough grazing before the bracken-filled gullies lead to the bleak hill tops. The heavy and persistent rain had stopped and now a cold front with rapidly clearing skies was dominant. I was naturally worried for Storm who for some time had been in the falsely warm environment of the lecture theatre. Gareth and Jane were most considerate and accommodating. Storm was not to remain isolated in our vehicle but still in her travelling crate, was to overnight in the comfort of an unused room in their farmhouse. Soon after bringing her inside, it was apparent that she had settled herself for the night. She had rolled up inside a spare dry towel, clearly very tired both after the long period of travelling and her many highly charged activities in front of the Trust's audience.

Our meal with Gareth and Jane was highlighted by the recalling of their recent but brief experience as stop-gap foster parents to Jarvis, a wild and orphaned dog otter cub, whom they had nurtured for a critical twelve days.

Late the previous autumn an adult bitch otter was found dead alongside the A40 trunk road near Crickhowell. The Brecknock Wildlife Trust has an otter group made up of some thirty-plus volunteers who have a particular interest in, and concern for, otters and more especially and vitally, the places where they live within the area covered by the Trust. After an immediate post mortem had been carried out by Adeline Bradshaw, who coordinates such work from her base at the Llysdinam Field Centre at Newbridge-on-Wye, it was confirmed that the bitch was lactating at the time of her death and therefore there was a strong possibility of orphaned cubs being somewhere in the close vicinity. Gareth and Jane were two of the enthusiasts whose local knowledge and special contacts might have been critical for any early discovery, particularly since they themselves had previously surveyed the Glanusk watershed and knew the location of several potential breeding holts.

The early searches sadly proved fruitless. But four days after the adult casualty had been reported an otter cub was seen following a duck along a nearby lane. The volunteer force, recruited by Diane Russell the Trust's administrator, swung into action. By good fortune the cub was handed to Stuart Jarvis the local estates gamekeeper, who had also been involved in the initial rescue attempts. A quick check-up by a veterinary surgeon was followed by Gareth and Jane taking Jarvis, suitably named after his rescuer, home to Llanbeilin which was to be his home for the next twelve days.

In between joining us to share the meal and then finishing the preparations for the next course, Gareth and Jane vividly related the important events of Jarvis's subsequent recovery in their house. I can clearly recall their intense vocabulary and descriptions of vital moments during his brief stay:

"I filled a syringe with fresh fish paste and baby milk mix as I had been advised...... he livened up very quickly and started sucking 20 mls at first, 40 mls two hours later...... his weight was 2lb 3ozs, he must have been two and a half to three months old, his eyes were still milky blue...... he was so weak that his stomach dragged along the carpet and he had several ticks around his eyes and in between his toes...... after every sleep I fully expected to find him dead...... Laura, our daughter, gave him a stuffed toy otter to cuddle...... soon he was eating small fish chopped up and was fighting with a furry glove puppet...... he had soon learnt to find his way back to his crate to sleep...... his intake of fish had increased rapidly and so had his strength...... he played in a series of cardboard tunnels but we always had to watch our fingers as he was capable of biting to the bone."

Gareth's and Jane's very committed involvement was clearly evident. At least an hour had now passed but when we heard that others had decided it was in Jarvis's best interests to be moved after only twelve days to another otter sanctuary many hundreds of miles away, a different language was apparent:

"We were convinced that such intensive care and handling was essential to his well-being, he needed company and we were better than nothing...... after he had been with us for such a short while we had to part with him at a motorway service station...... it had been a tremendous responsibility but a great privilege to have a wild otter in our temporary care...... I heard him bark with fright for the first time since we had taken him in...... I felt I had betrayed him."

Supper was now long finished and it had been a passionate story indeed, following what had also been for me an emotional evening working with Storm. Although very tired, hearing Jarvis's rescue story only served to remind me of the remarkable and quite personal events that eventually led to Storm and myself coming together over five years previously. Sadly and perhaps rather impolitely, I did not have the energy to relate and share that story with my hosts. I must have finally fallen asleep at about two o'clock in the morning.

The journey home to Cornwall from Brecon for Storm, Roger and myself was undertaken in completely contrasting weather conditions to the day before. At the farm gates that morning there were brief fond farewells with messages of good luck exchanged between us. We hoped Gareth and Jane would find continuing signs of otters returning to their original and nearby haunts of that part of mid-Wales; in return was their promise to keep us in touch with Jarvis's progress in the future. He had survived the journey, and now six months later was living with a young bitch otter. There was also the possibility that he would be returned complete with his new mate perhaps to share parenthood together in these beautiful upland valleys, where his mother's life had been cut short so tragically. Finally best wishes too, for my ongoing lecture work on behalf of British otters, always of course accompanied by Storm. Storm was, inevitably, accorded final glances of affection after an appearance, dare I say a performance, that had so captivated them the night before.

As we drove away in bright sunshine with clear blue skies overhead, the peaks of Cefn Clando and Ysuwydd Hwch, close to Llandefalle Hill, were reflected in the still and clear waters of Llangorse Lake. There was a strong feeling of calm and serenity around, although the bleakness of the moorland and crags reflected the harshness of the back end of the recent winter. At this height above sea-level, it would probably be at least another .

two months before the first real flush of spring colours would be reflected in the hedgerows and fields. Still time therefore, for Gareth and Jane to hopefully discover more tracks and signs before they became lost in the lush growth of spring and summer. Wild otters are elusive creatures, they are great wanderers yet so shy of man. Without any doubt, the wildness and mystery, and also the future survival of the beautiful British otter, had started to dominate both of their lives too.

Certainly that sense of the first day of spring in the air contributed to our travelling seeming to pass more quickly. The pressure and tensions had passed, there was the uplifting sensation of crossing the beautiful Severn Estuary this time, as planned, via the old bridge! Downstream lay the inspiring structure of the second Severn crossing stretching across to Wales from the Gloucestershire bank and in particular, from the green meadows around New Passage. There, as a youngster, I had frequently watched with my father from behind the sea wall, in every month of the year, the ever present curlew, redshank, lapwing, oyster-catcher and shelduck. Their wildness complimented the wide open tracts of the foreshore and the adjacent saltings. Was it here that the seed of an ambition to always live within sight and sound of such birds was sown? The Saturday or Sunday treat also took in a visit to see the ocean-going ships berthed in nearby Avonmouth Docks which lay a few miles to the south at the mouth of the River Avon. I had my spotters' guides for both birds and ships. Two small and slim paperbacks, illustrated with black and white photographs, listed the details for the latter not only of the small cargo boats that plied the coastal trade from the continent, Ireland and Scotland to the City docks of Bristol and the other Severn river harbours, but also the much larger freighters, tankers and tramp steamers that called from all over the globe. There were cargos of timber, grain, crude oil, refrigerated food and manufactured goods from the ports of every continent. A daily list of shipping movements was published in a local newspaper, the Western Daily Press, so I was able to excitedly forewarn my father of the particular ships still likely to be in port and which therefore could be 'ticked' over the forthcoming weekend.

Every time I cross either of the two bridges my thoughts usually reflect one of these two particularly strong childhood memories. It was no different today.

I recalled standing beneath the tall gaunt cranes as they unloaded from the ships' holds their cargoes directly into the adjacent warehouses or into the row upon row of waiting lorries and railway wagons which would then be taken further to inland destinations. The names of the regular 'Lines' still linger long in my memory. The Elder Dempster boats usually came from West Africa, with hard wood logs and cocoa beans; the Ellerman Line from East Africa with tobacco; the city of Bristol upstream had much of its workforce working in the world famous chocolate and tobacco factories of Fry's and WD & HO Wills. The Shaw Savill liners were bringing us ever increasing amounts of chilled lamb and dairy products from Australia and New Zealand but one of the highlights was to catch an Elders and Fyffes boat in port. They were quite distinctive with a bright yellow funnel contrasting against the white superstructure of the bridge. To be allowed to stand at the top of the ship's gangplank and watch the stems of green bananas being brought ashore which had been originally harvested in the islands of the West Indies was a real treat.

Other equally vivid and wonderful memories flooded back as I glanced upstream of the old bridge. To the north beyond the stark and modern concrete outcrops that are both Oldbury and Berkeley nuclear power stations, I imagined, given the time of year, just what birds were making the upper reaches of the Severn estuary towards Gloucester their home. The Dumbles, or New Grounds, are the lush cattle meadows and grazing saltmarshes that have formed part of the Berkeley Estates since medieval times, and which for the past fifty years have been under the trusteeship of the Wildfowl and Wetlands Trust. On that marvellous spring morning there could well have been the last remnants of the large wintering flock of European white-fronted geese from Russia still grazing behind the sea-wall; perhaps also in the wet flashes and ruts of the fields would be the first of the godwits on passage, along with greenshank and ruff, all restless as the urge to continue their spring migration from African shores to their northern breeding grounds in Iceland and Spitzbergen became ever more dominant. Constantly preening and hesitant to leave finally, their daily feeding cycle would be controlled by the rise and fall of the tides of the Severn Estuary. However whatever the month the resident waders and duck would still be there, just as they were in the late 40s and early 50s when their ancestors gave me so many thrills at an early age. They were exciting birds, close at hand in exciting places; I was fascinated by the mysteries of their migrations, by the routines of their daily lives dominated by the ebb and flow of the tides. I lived only a short distance away in the heart of a very large city, but there was much at which to marvel and the birds were first identified by using my other trusty pocket guide, 'The Observers Book of Birds'.

I felt very good as I crossed back into home territory, and later that evening I still felt on top of the world. When passing Bristol I had stopped to visit my elderly parents, albeit very briefly, in order to update them on the news from Cornwall and Brecon. Then I dropped Roger at his home in north Cornwall and pressed on in order to release and feed Storm. But I made sure there was still time available to recount the events of the past two days to my daughter Olivia. She always, quite rightly, insisted on the greatest detail in answer to her many questions. That night she really had waited up far too late with school the next day, but following her there were even more recollections to share with my wife Helen.

Very early the following morning, after Olivia had left by bus for Truro High School, Helen and I were walking our English springer spaniel Sasha on one of the deserted beaches close to our home. We do this regularly during winter term-time. The half-hour or so it takes us to wander the tideline of the sandy cove and back again gives us time for close reflection together and an opportunity to enjoy Sasha's apparently unlimited energy and fun. Early every morning we will wander together and always in a special light; sometimes we will experience totally contrasting light in the space of a few minutes. These moments remind us why we have chosen to leave our roots and closest families in Bristol and north Somerset to give ourselves and most particularly Olivia, an even better quality of life in Cornwall.

It also happens that another lure of this particular beach in wintertime, is the frequent and close proximity of guillemots and razorbills fishing well inshore for small fish in the gentle surf. Sand-eels and sprats are their favourite, as they are for so many other animals and birds around our islands. Sand-eels are one of the building blocks of all marine life yet their numbers are in serious decline both from man's over-fishing and other, as yet unidentified, reasons. With often no one else around, we can observe the auks in great detail as they swim sometimes no more than a few feet away. Their confidence and apparent lack of concern for Sasha as she scampers and chases nearby to retrieve encourages the closeness of occasional exciting rarities. Over-wintering grebes and divers, so difficult to distinguish at long range, and here in west Cornwall at the extent of their southerly winter migration in these islands, frequently appear too. In the days before leaving for Brecon, Helen and I had been watching a lone great northern diver. At this time of year it is silent, but in two months time the loon's haunting call, which once heard can never be forgotten, would be echoing across some fresh water loch in Scotland, maybe on Islay in the Inner Hebrides, where many years previously Helen and I had sought them in their summer haunts. For several mornings, we had eagerly scoured the inshore waters on our arrival and had after spotting him or her, always planned our movements across the sands so as to subtly approach as close as possible. At the same time, we would try to keep as much of the early morning light as possible behind us in order to improve our observation.

"It's in really close again this morning," started Helen excitedly as she glanced seawards.

I locked the car and hurried to use the field glasses.

"It was in just about the same position yesterday. I had a really good view and it took no notice of Sasha. But I didn't see it in the heavy rain of Wednesday when you were travelling."

"I wasn't seeing that much either," I replied jokingly, "especially when we took the wrong road for the old bridge; and I can't see much now either," I added in a more serious tone a few seconds later. "Has Olivia by any chance been using the glasses because I seem unable to focus them properly?"

"No way," answered Helen rather sarcastically, "they've been where you always leave them. What's the problem?"

The next conversation I clearly remember that day was at around six o'clock in the evening with the doctors at Falmouth Eye Hospital. The word cataract had initially been mentioned at the local surgery after I had hurriedly returned from the beach. Now the conversation was altogether on a more serious level.

"But I remember no pain" I interrupted.

"No you wouldn't have done," added Nick Wilson-Holt, the surgeon with whom luckily I had more than the initial rapport of patient and specialist since two of his young family were with Olivia at school. "Sadly you have suffered a slight stroke, there has been a hardening of the arteries and a severe breakdown in the blood vessels behind the retina of your left eye. I must tell you that almost certainly, you have permanently lost the sight in that eye."

I was feeling very shocked to say the least. When we had first met an hour or so earlier we had immediately recognised one another because of the Truro High School connection. I had said something like 'so you are the parent who is the ophthalmic surgeon' and he had replied "and you are the father who chases around lecturing with a live otter.' It was about my work with and for otters that he continued in more serious vein.

"I am afraid that's the end of long motorway journeys, followed by becoming pumped up with adrenalin as you lecture with this otter of yours."

"Storm, that's her name," I interrupted quickly, "the only British otter with a licence from English Nature to......

"A change in your immediate lifestyle is going to be the order of the day," Mr Wilson-Holt pressed on, "and my brief now is to ensure that what has sadly happened to your left eye is not repeated in the other. Otherwise we will have a serious problem on our hands. It's going to be up to you to ring the necessary changes. Meanwhile I will be organising the necessary laser treatment to be carried out on you under general anaesthetic at Treliske Hospital as soon as possible."

I was most subdued that evening with Helen and Olivia. Unobtrusively I kept shutting my good right eye in the hope that the blur in the left was just a bad dream. There was the inevitable small talk between the three of us as both Helen and Olivia tried to reassure me each in their separate ways. Typically and as always so spontaneously, Olivia's response was several of her all embracing hugs before she went to bed. I was comforted in the knowledge that Helen who had always supported me so loyally and lovingly through other problems would broach the subject of what I should do next in the cold light of the following day, and only during Olivia's absence at school.

Later that night, before finally joining Helen I went and sat with Storm. It was necessary and comforting to do something that was so much part of my regular daily, or as in this case, night-time routine.

Storm was full of life again, having out of necessity slept soundly through the previous night and the whole of the following day after her exertions away from home. She greeted me excitedly but was also very quick to pick up my tension.

"You are not your normal self," she started, "something is bothering you isn't it, please tell me".

I quickly, but briefly, related the events of the past few hours to Storm. However, and as with Olivia, I didn't try to pretend or mislead. Not surprisingly her response was as positive as Olivia's.

"But are you going to be alright"?, she enquired.

"Less tension and stress in order to achieve a much lower level of blood pressure by pursuing a different life-style. They are the aspects of my present life where there must be major changes in the future"

"Will we still live in Cornwall, or will we have to move? You see I have grown to like it here already."

Now I could see her anxiety rising, and as with Olivia an hour or so earlier, I moved quickly on to a more positive approach.

"Don't think about all these possible negative factors," I said. "I was waiting around for a considerable time today for various tests to be carried out; it gave me a good chance to think about the future. Therefore, I want to ask you a favour."

I sensed Storm's immediate curiosity. At that moment she was listening to me as she lay on top of her travelling crate. I was sitting alongside her and truthfully she could not have been closer.

"I am going to ask you to tell me your life story, down to every little detail you can remember," I whispered.

"You mean from the moment I was born," said Storm excitedly.

"That's right, and from what you tell me I am going to write a book. I also plan to include other experiences from the thirty years I have spent with otters. When I join you late at night you can start reminiscing, doesn't matter about the sequence as I can make notes about the stories, both yours and mine. Then I will put them together in some semblance of order. The details will come later. After that I will set out to find a possible publisher."

"This is going to be fun," added Storm enthusiastically. "We should have plenty to tell between us. I would love everybody to know where I came from, I could describe my mother and why I am actually here with you right now, and everything that has happened to us. When are we going to start? You could go and fetch a pen and paper right now."

It was uncanny how at that moment Storm sounded just like Olivia again, immediately jumping onto a new idea or suggestion and always, impatiently, wanting to fulfill it straight away.

"No, not tonight," I cautioned, "I am feeling fairly shell-shocked just now and I still haven't physically recovered from the Brecon trip. You start thinking about all you want to tell me. In fact I know what you can do first – think of a title!"

Storm was now rushing around all over the place. She plunged into her tank and kicked hard with her rear legs, reappearing only briefly on the surface before diving again. I rolled up one shirt sleeve and immersed a bare arm into the tank for her to brush against it, and quickly she realised that I was preparing to join in with her as usual. Immediately she was out of the water onto her favourite towel. She went into her regular and vigorous rubbing routine before chasing back to plunge into the tank and so start the sequence all over again.

Fascinated by her as always, I watched her sleepily. Inevitably, I began to ponder again the consequences of the events of the last three days.

I was startled back into full consciousness by a very wet Storm bouncing into my lap as she raced on to the top of her travelling crate.

"I have clean forgotten your food, you must be very hungry. I can fetch it immediately. It's all prepared. Then I will lock up for the night and I shall see you in the morning."

"Don't you mean later this morning?" was Storm's reply.

It was only then that I realised that I had not just dozed with Storm as I had imagined. I had slept soundly for several hours whilst she had played. Now I had to be careful not to waken Helen and Olivia on my return indoors. The weather was changing again; the clear frosty night in the Brecon mountains seventy-two hours earlier was being replaced by ever thickening layers of cloud spilling in from the west. That first burst of almost summer sun glimpsed in the Welsh hills and hugely enjoyed would soon be forgotten. It would be raining again by the time Helen and I took Olivia to the school bus stop in just a couple of hours time.

"Don't forget to think of a title for the book," were my last words to Storm who was still very active.

"I have already been doing that," she replied, as, in the half-light, she surfaced with her head dripping wet. "How about *Stormforce*?"

As I made my way to bed, I thought that sounded rather appropriate.

AND NOW THE SHIPPING FORECAST ISSUED BY THE MET.
OFFICE AT 1725 ON FRIDAY 17TH FEBRUARY 1993

THERE ARE WARNINGS OF GALES IN PLYMOUTH BISCAY
FINISTERRE SOLE LUNDY FASTNET IRISH SEA SHANNON
ROCKALL MALIN HEBRIDES BAILEY FAEROES SOUTH EAST
ICELAND

THE GENERAL SYNOPSIS AT MIDDAY

DEVELOPING ATLANTIC LOW MOVING RAPIDLY NORTHWEST
EXPECTED NORTH OF FAROES 953 BY MIDDAY TOMORROW.
HIGH DOGGER 1043 SLOW MOVING WITH LITTLE CHANGE

THE AREA FORECAST FOR THE NEXT 24 HOURS

BISCAY FINISTERRE SOLE LUNDY
SOUTHWEST VEERING WEST OR NORTHWEST 7 TO SEVERE GALE
9. INCREASING STORMFORCE 10 LATER. RAIN THEN SQUALLY
WINTRY SHOWERS. MODERATE OR POOR BECOMING MAINLY
GOOD

FASTNET IRISH SEA SHANNON . . . .

THREE

"ARE YOU SURE IT'S NOT A MINK"

"**W**ould you believe I've just taken a message from a woman who thinks she has a baby otter cub?" my wife Helen exclaimed excitedly.

It was very early on a cold mid-February morning when my everyday routine was shattered by the shrill bell of the outside telephone.

"Project Otter," I had initially announced, picking up the receiver as best as I could, for at that moment I was busily preparing brown trout and sand-eels for our otters' daily meal.

"Where was she calling from?" I enquired in astonishment.

"I'm not very sure but as far as I can gather the cub was found somewhere on Exmoor early yesterday morning. The woman and her husband, well they're keeping it warm in their kitchen, and are trying to bottle-feed it. They think it's an otter cub but obviously they're not certain."

"You questioned them about its colour, didn't you?" I interrupted rather abruptly, "and surely they told you how big it is."

"Hang on a second," Helen replied, "give me a chance. They want you to go and see it as soon as possible. They didn't receive much help from the various organisations they originally contacted until the Otter Trust gave them Ken's number in Cornwall. It was he who put them in touch with us." Ken Hill is the manager at the Tamar Otter Sanctuary at North Petherwin, near Launceston in Cornwall.

"Well, there's no way I can leave here until I've finished feeding. Will you ring her back straight away? Tell her I will come as soon as possible and I need really accurate directions? Then as soon as I am through here, I'll drop by via the farm and collect the details before leaving."

I hurried on with my work. I had several otters to feed and

bed down. The weather had been typically very wet and cold for the time of year with strong gale-force winds over the previous seventy-two hours. I could not easily shorten the time it took to prepare the precise diet that I gave to our otters every day, and I reckoned it would be at least one o'clock before I could leave for our home which was some seven miles away in north Somerset.

Nevertheless I set to work with increased vigour. I needed to concentrate and to take special care whilst cutting the fish. Many a time previously I had removed a slice of skin from a finger when not paying full attention. But now my mind was really distracted and if I was not careful in the next couple of hours a similar accident would again be on the cards.

I was full of excitement at the prospect of possibly seeing my first wild otter cub in a very long time. Then it had been Boxing Day 1966 when Bob Cooke, a man of the marshes, rang me from his remote cottage on the north Norfolk coast. I had met both him and his wife Joan a few years earlier and prior to my three years at university; he bred wildfowl as a hobby and I had acquired many young birds from him for my own collection. But that day, in late December, his message was that whilst checking the coastline, for he was also an auxiliary coastguard, he had spotted a very wet half-grown otter cub stranded in a tidal creek on Salthouse marsh. His English springer spaniel had successfully 'fetched', so could I come and collect it straightaway.

Now some twenty five years later, would history repeat itself? Were these people sure it was not a mink? That's why I had asked Helen the critical question about the cub's colour. Wild mink are black; an adult otter can reflect all the colours of the wild mushroom; in certain light the coat really does have an almost pinkish tinge, particularly to the soft-fur of the underbody. However, otter cubs are born blind and helpless with soft grey velvety fur and weigh seventy-eight grams. They have rather square muzzles, tiny ears, small pads and are blessed with half-webbed feet, all of which are pink in colour. They suckle every two or three hours, pressing the bitch's stomach with their front paws; their little tails wag and as their mother moves to re-settle, the cubs will call softly.

Their development is slow; their eyes open when they are about five weeks old and weaning begins at seven weeks. From about ten weeks they will eat solid food more regularly. But they will continue to be nursed for up to six months and will not finally split from their mother until a year after they are born.

62

Size clearly differentiates otters from mink. Some male otters are really large animals and when handling a 'Ministry' mink trap you are suddenly aware that an adult otter would be hard pushed to insert just its head and shoulders into the opening.

I reflected momentarily on some of the reports we had received in the intervening years of the possible sightings of otters. Had they not all been mink? Numerous callers had enthusiastically described in great detail having an otter on their lawn, or in a nearby pond or ditch. No further questioning was usually necessary after quickly establishing that the colour was inevitably described as black; subsequently telling the caller that a dog otter could measure up to four feet long from tip of nose to tip of tail, and could weigh between twenty to twenty-five pounds finally gave the game away and had usually curtailed every enquiry. I have always thought that if someone was really looking at an otter, then on the size factor alone, callers would more than likely report its occurrence to the police first!

Sadly there have also been the occasions when a fatality is reported. These calls are on the increase as otters slowly recover their numbers and return to old traditional haunts. Most reflect road casualties; one recently was on a little used lane close to our recent home near Mark on the north Somerset Levels, and another fatality was in similarly remote countryside close to a tributary of the Eastern Cleddau, near Milford Haven in Pembrokeshire. I recalled hearing with utter disbelief the story of a motorcyclist arriving at the home of a taxidermist near Umberleigh in mid-Devon with a dead otter strapped to his back; although yet again the victim of a road accident, it was remarkably unmarked hence the value of preserving the carcase. Close by and unbelievably only days later, two dog otters were so much at loggerheads with one another as they attempted to define their respective but adjacent territories, that they were unable to drag themselves apart to avoid the fast approaching danger. Both were killed instantly on the railway tracks of the 'Tarka' line that follows the valley of the River Exe, and which links north and south Devon between Barnstaple and Exeter .

Meanwhile I had finished preparing the otters' fish, and with the accompanying portions of meat already prepared, there was a flurry of activity on my part. Another half-hour and every individual had been fed and their enclosures locked. I took out the next day's food to thaw and after a couple of last minute checks, for I had a nasty habit of failing to secure the most vital bolts when distracted, I was away to the farm and Helen and hopefully, my further instructions. By now I was very excited but rather apprehensive at the outcome of the next few hours.

Helen had sandwiches, a flask of hot soup and full direction details ready and I soon realised there was the best part of a two hour journey ahead in our Bedford Midi one ton van. Much of the latter part of the journey would be slow through narrow lanes, particularly as I neared my destination, and as daylight was not on my side I also needed to avoid making any major mistakes.

The couple who had found this tiny creature lived in the Brendon Hills close to the Somerset and Devon border. The quickest route initially would be south on the M5, leaving the motorway at the Wellington turn-off, then through Wiveliscombe and on into the hills. From there it would be a case of following their instructions closely, so I glanced quickly at a more detailed map to acquaint myself with the last stretch. It seemed that my eventual destination would not be that far from Wimbleball and Clatworthy reservoirs.

"Just you concentrate now, and don't get distracted thinking about otters," suggested Helen as she leant over the farm gate.

I started the vehicle's engine in order to leave, but she was determined to continue and this time rather more firmly.

"Have an accident, and you won't have any wild otter to look after. That's of course, if it is one. I expect after all this fuss it will turn out to be yet another mink, as on all the other occasions."

"Okay, okay," I interrupted, "I am listening to you but I'd better be on my way."

"And think of Olivia, too, when you're driving; she wants a daddy in one piece when she gets home from school. Don't you forget what I've told you. Anyway, I hope you're lucky this time. See you later, and call me!"

With her final warnings ringing in my ears I was away from the farm gateway, and five minutes later I was joining the slip-road on the M5 at junction 22. I was heading south into Somerset on my journey to discover what in fact this tiny creature was, mink or otter. I arranged my sandwiches and drink between the driving and the passenger seats in the front central compartment of the van and settled down to complete the first thirty miles or so on the relatively easy stretch of the motorway. I was aware of the persistent heavy rain, and the strongly gusting westerly winds were all the more noticeable with my relatively high-sided vehicle.

The weather was very cold.

It was inevitable however, as I relaxed, that I would recall the only other occasion I had travelled to see a wild otter cub. Then my mission was to collect a young creature that had already been correctly identified. Now I was going to look at something, which as Helen had already clearly reminded me, could well turn out to be a mink. The details to hand so far were sketchy, but I was prepared, yet again, to put any doubts aside as I started to hasten further south. Indeed, ignoring my wife's warnings, I allowed myself to cast my mind back. That first journey, ever alone returning with a half-grown otter cub, was dramatic enough to have remained deeply etched on my mind ever since.

That phone call had come when, with my family, we were concluding Boxing Day lunch. I had come down from Cambridge eighteen months previously and was in the process of creating my Wildlife Park in Westbury-on Trym, Bristol; the Park was to be opened to the general public six months hence in June 1967 by my then schoolboy hero, Peter Scott.

The first aviaries, enclosures and pools were already under construction and I had already been away on several exciting trips fetching various species of animals and birds. I was to specialise in keeping and breeding only British or native wildlife, and that morning had been feeding and bedding down some of the recent acquisitions. I had made many friends in Norfolk from those Cambridge days where I had planned my future life and work. My first fallow deer fawns had come from the Earl of Leicester's estate at Holkham Hall; they had then been bottle-reared, and now formed the nucleus of a splendid little herd, all of them blessed with the pale true 'menil' colour. From my love of west and mid Wales I had become inspired by one of the leading naturalists of the day, a never to be forgotten acquaintance with the seabird authority, Ronald Lockley. He had pioneered the original studies in the 1930s of the seabirds that inhabit the islands of Skomer and Skokholm. He had also become a leading expert on Atlantic grey seals. His postcard had summoned me post-haste to his cottage at Marloes, near Martinshaven in Pembrokeshire, to collect Dick, not an Atlantic grey pup as I had expected, but a young orphaned common seal. Dick had been rescued after becoming stranded away from one of the large breeding colonies of common seals to be found on the sands of the Wash in Lincolnshire. He had been transferred to far west Wales to be nurtured back to full health. The fallow deer and Dick, along with some other common seals who were also maturing with him in the same pool, were two of the groups of animals with whom I had already spent very good company earlier that morning.

Bob had briefly reported that he had been walking the nearby saltmarsh and the adjacent coastal shingle ridge close to his home. This he did regularly at first light every day, at the same time exercising his dog. For no particular reason that morning, and as luck would have it, he took a different route. Much later he had decided to return skirting a marsh that was split by a main freshwater drainage ditch, and via a track which gave him, at the same time, a close view of the top end of the tidal creek. Just as he was turning for home he had spotted it, a half-grown otter cub, apparently exhausted and soaking wet, lying amongst the debris that is found at the top of the tide. It was so distressed that his dog had retrieved it without fuss, although the springer had needed all its expertise to cope with the soft mud. Bob had experienced no difficulty in tucking it inside his duffel coat next to his heavy duty all weather clothing. On his return, he had immediately wrapped it in a couple of old sweaters and had placed it on a bed of towels in a cardboard box. Safe next to the all-night stove, his instincts told him it might now stand a chance of surviving in that warmth, but there would have been none at all if it had been left exposed to the winter's elements out on the marsh. The weather was bitterly cold and as he returned to his cottage close to the coast road, further heavy rain had started.

"Can you come and collect it as soon as possible?" he had enquired.

"Yes, of course," I replied instantly, and almost before his question was finished.

"The sooner it's being properly cared for the better," he had continued. "When do you think you could come? Joan and I will obviously do our best in the meantime."

"I can come straightaway, now, this afternoon," I interrupted again.

"That would be best; the sooner it's safe in a new and stable environment with you, the sooner it might recover from its setback. You're very welcome to stay overnight."

"I'll be on my way as soon as I am organised and I'll try and be with you by late tonight. I'll ring if there are any problems," I added excitedly as I returned to the dining table.

A few minutes later the implications of his unexpected call

were sinking in; a possible otter cub as the latest arrival for my Park, and in the middle of winter too, just when you least expected to be offered a wild creature. The possible exception would have been seabirds, perhaps guillemots or razorbills, victims of some rogue oil slick, or stormbound. Everybody, including our guests, joined in helping me prepare for an imminent departure; my mother put up some food for the journey and my father made numerous phone calls to discover to discover the whereabouts of the nearest petrol station that might be open on this Bank Holiday. Both the tank and a spare can for the long journey needed to be filled. It was a journey which without hold-ups would take the rest of that day and evening. The final miles would be through the lonely and deserted lanes of rural north Norfolk, not a trip to be normally undertaken in poor weather, ever alone in the height of winter.

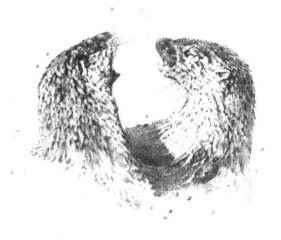

Bob's phone call, as with today's message, had been very brief, with no more than the bare details. It was important to think and plan rationally. I would surely need a travelling crate; what and when was I going to try and feed the cub; was it still on its mother's milk or would it eat solid food, fish perhaps? A suitable box was eventually found, as were some straw bales to pack around it as extra insulation; I eased out a couple of frozen mackerel and herring from much larger stone packs, fish that I already had in store for my seals. I asked my father to find a chemist or to check with a local hospital early the following morning after the Bank Holiday break, in order to obtain some dried milk and a bottle feeder ready for my return. The cub could well have been younger than Bob at first thought.

Suddenly there was no more time to plan. It was already early afternoon and I needed to be on my way out of Bristol along the Cotswold hills, through Tetbury and Cirencester, to pick up the A40 Cheltenham road towards Oxford. Then, it would be across middle England through the towns of Witney, Newport Pagnell and Bedford and on towards Cambridge and the flatter lands of East Anglia. Admittedly it was a route I already knew from going backwards and forwards to University. From Cambridge and Newmarket and beyond, heading further east was another already familiar stretch too. I had started buying fish wholesale for my seals, and in particular Hebridean herring from Frank Petersen, a merchant in Grimsby's fish dock. But after reaching Cambridge, that route took me in a more northerly direction towards Ely, Boston and the Lincolnshire Wolds.

I have no real recollection over thirty years later of most of that journey across central England, except that the weather seemed to be worsening, was becoming steadily colder and wetter, and that the already poor daylight of that Boxing Day afternoon, had soon vanished. What does stay quite dramatically in my mind, though, was the final few miles through the lanes from Holt along the valley of the River Glaven, before meeting the coastal road running from Blakeney through to Cley-next-the-Sea. Bob and Joan's cottage would be eventually found at the far end of the magnificent blanket of coastal marsh and reclaimed fields that lie behind the shingle ridge at Salthouse. Thence the road would climb inland towards the holiday resorts of Sheringham and Cromer.

By now it was very late, gone eleven o'clock, and with over two hundred and fifty miles already on the clock, I used my previous knowledge of those lanes to avoid going through the small market town of Holt. Some five years before, in the spring of 1961, I had left Clifton College to work with the naturalist Philip Wayre for two summers at his Norfolk home, and which was not that far from the coast. During my following under-graduate days I began to explore further the haunts with which I had only fleetingly become acquainted. Indeed, I had originally become aware of those north Norfolk marshes while still at school, and with my parents had enjoyed a summer caravan holiday close to Blakeney. I spent hours seeking out the bearded tits in the reedbeds of Cley marsh, although the real treat on that first occasion had been to travel from Bristol via the River Orwell which lay much further south in Suffolk. My father had planned as a complete surprise an overnight stay close to Havergate Island to ensure that I recorded my first avocets that summer.

So inevitably the lure of East Anglia was great. Holt, and more particularly the Feathers Inn, had become for me the place to socialise out of term time with new friends of similar interests. However, in the pitch black of this wild winter's night, I sensed that most sensible souls would have been indoors, closeted around a roaring winter fire.

There was no doubt in my mind that the wind had now strengthened to a severe gale; there were frequent squally gusts which served to focus my mind on the fact that, at long last, I was coming close to my goal. Now the tiredness that had set in during the rather long and monotonous haul through the flat lands of Cambridgeshire had passed and I was fully alert again.

I recalled how Bob had previously recounted to me tales of the otters that frequent the water meadows and fresh-water drains of the empty north Norfolk marshes with their endless reedbeds and tidal creeks. These stretch for miles from Scolt Head Island to the west to the last of the drainage ditches which divide the meadows used for the summer grazing in the east. Bob and his wife Joan lived in a two storey cottage that looked out over this wildlife haven towards vast shingle ridge that protected them and the other homes that hugged the coast road, from the worst of the ravages of the North Sea storms. These originate hundreds of miles away to the north in the Arctic .

The young store cattle grazing contentedly in summer-time would be buzzed by the breeding lapwings, and the male redshanks would 'bob' characteristically on prominent grassy tussocks as they guarded their nesting territories in the long grass. In the reeds and rushes above water covered in a blanket of duckweed, summer warblers and garganey teal from Africa would join the resident wild duck and moorhens. In the densest vegetation were those elusive bearded tits, with their distinctive long tails and black moustaches, and which I had first sought out several years previously. Between the grazed fields and the high shingle ridges lay large stretches of brackish lagoons, waters that would only be topped up by the highest in the monthly cycle of tides. Here amongst the sedge tussocks and patches of shingle carpeted in places by plants such as rest-harrow and sea campion, were the various breeding colonies of the little and sandwich terns, black-headed gulls, and the occasional nesting scrapes of oyster catchers and ringed plovers. The terns would flight during every daylight hour to Blakeney and to the tidal channel that led to the open sea for the tempting targets of tiny sand-eels.

In winter the farm stock and the summer bird-watchers deserted the marshes, and the solitude was only occasionally shattered by a weekend wildfowler. On that night the nearest rutted and waterlogged fields to the road, and the ditches which were lying almost brimful, were home to a host of wigeon and teal, and to many sheltering waders and winter migrants. Some of the latter would have been very rare. Windswept, desolate and very cold, I was surprised the marshes were so well favoured by all and sundry, unless of course you had climbed the protective shingle ridge and had suffered the full blast of the arctic wind as it whipped in off the North Sea.

At the end of my first autumn term at Pembroke College I travelled with my father to stay with Brent Pope, a personal friend who was the owner of the Manor Hotel, Blakeney. The plan was to observe during the short daylight hours the hordes of wintering Russian dark-bellied brent geese feeding at low water on the local Zostera beds. We spent one evening with Bob and Joan and then on our way back along the coast road to the hotel, took one of the few road tracks across the marsh to climb the shingle ridge in the darkness of the night. The roar of the onshore gale and the crashing of the waves became ever more intense but little did we imagine, as we fought our way up through the soft shingle, the total shock that was in store for us. As we reached the crest of the beach we were struck by an unbelievably intense cold blast. You could lean at almost forty-five degrees forward into the gale. In moments the cold had cut right through us. Quickly we made our way back to the safety of the car, and as we left I pictured all the teal tucked up in the reedbeds in the lee of the shingle ridge; the relative calm within the dense cover of swaying phragmites must have been sheer bliss compared to the arctic blast not a quarter of a mile distant.

I remembered suddenly braking hard to turn right to join the main coastal road from Blakeney. There was no oncoming traffic that late at night, and I was down the short hill to cross the river Glaven where the sluice gates keep the ebb and flow of the tidal waters of the marshes apart from the fresh water streams of the meadows. Little did I realise then, that at this road bridge more than one dog otter was to lose his life in later years as he tracked his territory. Next it was sharp left, and through Cley past the windmill and church, with welcoming lights still lit late in a few homes. As I broke cover from the village I passed the last cottages on the higher ground on my right and with the marshes coming up on my left, I suddenly felt the storm with dramatic effect.

The van lurched as the ferocity and the force of the threatening gale was thrown against the side of the vehicle. I put the windscreen wipers in overdrive as the squally rain turned to sleet. The late night temperatures had dropped fast. Rain, wind and sleet, everything seemed to be coming from over my left shoulder, lashing against the passenger window of the van as I tried to hurry the last couple of miles to my destination. My heart was beating faster now for my expectations had been building rapidly since passing Holt a few miles back. The excitement had dried my mouth. Even in the darkness I recognised the village duck pond of Salthouse but further away, marshside, I could not make anything out clearly. There was nothing but the sound of wind and rain.

Then it was a right-hand indicator before the final braking and suddenly I was, at long last, swinging up into the welcoming shelter of the courtyard alongside Bob's cottage. I was late, very late, but I had made it. It was almost midnight.

I grabbed my overnight bag, locked the van and ran into the lower porch to escape the elements.

"Come ya in David," Joan called out from the top of the stairs, "you've been a long while, we'd given you up for lost. It's a terrible night out there. You'll have a cup of tea, something to eat?"

The living-room was a snug fortress against the wild elements that the North Sea throws against the east coast, and as I stepped into its warm glow there was Bob, relaxed as always, in his favourite armchair. His face broke into a slight smile, and with a twinkle in his eyes both of mischief and affection he greeted me.

"How ya doing then?," he enquired in his soft Norfolk accent.

"Fine," I replied, "just fine, although very cold. But I'll warm up in here in no time."

Everything happened for Bob and Joan in their living room. You ate and drank, talked the wildlife of the marshes thereabouts, and mutually recalled the recent news since the last visit. Either their springer spaniel or the jack russell sat on your lap, and the whole comfortable scene was supervised by the ever happy Joan, aided and abetted by a knowing and talkative mynah bird, who would eye you so closely from his special perch. The room was packed full of their personal memorabilia, photographs, paintings, and mementoes gathered from here and there over the years; every guest just dropped deep into the nearest settee and immediately became part of the friendly scene.

The living room was at first floor level, simply because there is always the continual threat of a tidal surge in the North Sea breaking the sea defences, as it had done on a dreadful winter's night some fifteen years previously. Then there had been a terrible loss of life, property and livestock. On the outside wall of the cottage is a marker at an unbelievable height, indicating the level the waters reached after breaking through the shingle ridge. It was frightening to imagine that at the peak of that storm and at the full tidal surge, there was nothing but the sea for mile upon mile, lying to a depth of several feet. On a previous visit, I had stood outside the cottage overlooking the marshes, and had suddenly become aware how far I was above the present coast road, which in turn lies well above the adjacent marshes. The stark reality of that unforeseen distaster was quite unsettling.

"I can do you eggs and bacon," called Joan from by the stove, "in the meantime here's your tea. Get that down you straight away, I should think you need it. Then have another with your meal."

"Have you ever seen an otter cub before?" interrupted Bob,

"No, never," I said, "I was hoping perhaps ....."

"Of course you can, she's wrapped up in some of my old sweaters. It's a bitch cub by the way, and she's in a box close to the all night boiler. When I picked her up after the dog had fetched her, she was wet through and cold, but I quickly wrapped her inside my jacket and hurried home. She's been hidden under my clothes since and has dried off remarkably well. Her breathing is now quite regular and she's much bigger than I originally thought. I guess she's ten or maybe even twelve weeks of age."

Although Bob continued to recall the details of the events that had led to her recovery earlier in the day, I had no eye contact

72

with him, and found myself quite simply staring at this beautiful little creature. From above, she appeared to be a deep chocolate brown colour, but as I observed her more closely, and as she occasionally changed her position, I began to appreciate the more delicate shades of lighter brown and grey of her underbody hair and of her inner coat.

"I reckon she's a brave little bitch but by following her mother was rather too bold for her own good," Bob continued. "The holts and the couches where the bitch is lying up with the cubs, and there are sure to be several, must be way out on the marsh. Although the cub could probably swim, she either could not keep up with the bitch, or mother and cub simply became separated by a strong ebbing tide in the main channel. When the tide turns here you know, the waters quickly drain away. I've rarely seen a cub on the outer marshes at this age; it probably tired quickly, became increasingly waterlogged and found herself stranded away from cover. A heavy drizzle backed by a cold and rapidly strengthening north-easterly wind, had set in over the coastal ridge very early this morning, and she quickly became saturated. She was lucky I found her when I did and that my dog could reach her across the soft mud."

Still I was not really listening to Bob. Here at my feet was a most lovely and delicate creature. She was fast asleep, curled up ever so tightly like so many family pussycats, in the position which in later years I was to come to know so well.

"I still can't believe it," I responded, repeating myself yet again. "Have you fed her?" However before Bob could respond Joan was interrupting.

"Are you going to come and eat your food? Little-un will be best off asleep 'til morning."

It was one of the most enjoyable and satisfying bacon and eggs suppers I've ever enjoyed, especially at that hour in the morning.

Not long later I was fading fast in my sleeping bag. An otter cub was something totally new to me and was instantly most captivating. As I rapidly lost consciousness I had no idea whatsoever how much the skill of Bob's springer way out on Salthouse marsh earlier that Boxing Day, was to influence my future.

73

FOUR

"ALL OTTERS NEED THEIR FAIR SHARE OF LUCK"

Suddenly I was again aware of the purpose of my present journey, of the continuing poor weather, and of the need to continue to make good time in order to discover as much as possible about the young creature which had been rescued. If it were an otter cub, then identifying it would only be the start of an involved and lengthy process of ensuring its ongoing survival. As I took the slip road south from the motorway into Wellington, I left behind my thoughts of the Norfolk journey some thirty years ago.

Wellington's town centre is relatively empty of traffic these days since the construction of the nearby motorway leading to the south-west. The M5 now by-passes it and the other busy market towns of Bridgwater, Taunton and Cullompton. We used to crawl through Wellington on our way to summer school holidays in Devon and Cornwall. We always seemed to take an age, all day in fact sometimes, crawling to our destination as my father negotiated the A38, the longest lane in Europe. Bude, with its nearby surfing beach at Crooklets, and with its distant views of magical Lundy on clear days was the family favourite on the Atlantic coast, as were the creeks and sandy coves of the estuary close to Kingsbridge and Salcombe, overlooking the English Channel.

I do not remember in any detail the last few miles to my destination that afternoon, unlike those of the seemingly never ending journey to north Norfolk for my first otter cub so many years previously. Maybe it was because this journey was so much shorter, and there was not the time to relax and let the miles go by; maybe it was because on this occasion, I was still unsure that I was not going to be shown yet another mink kitten.

However the directions had been simple and clear-cut. Soon I was making my way across a garden lawn towards the back door of a cottage. I was surprised to see aviaries housing hawks and owls, and at that moment was completely unaware of their significance. I was greeted by Francesca and Graham and immediately shown into the kitchen. The introductions were brief and the formalities necessarily concise.

"She's over here," started Francesca softly, "we're pretty certain it's....."

I glanced quickly and apprehensively into the box, as Francesca gently lifted the tiny animal clear of the bundle of makeshift bedding.

"Yes, that's an otter cub for sure," I interrupted her immediately.

"She is very weak," Francesca continued, stroking the cub tenderly. "However, she's taken a little milk and she's now much warmer too." I was quickly appreciating that the little creature was in very caring hands. "I was just about to prepare her another drink. But it seems quite a struggle for her to take as much as I would wish. It hardly seems enough to keep body and soul together, and that worries me." Francesca's tone was reflecting her obvious anxiety. "However, while I'm about it, I'll put the kettle on at the same time. You'll have a cup of tea? won't you," she continued.

I was standing very still looking at the tiny cub. She seemed, well she seemed to me older than her size indicated. She was all head and shoulders with disturbingly, very little body weight. I was still quietly working out what might have happened to her in the previous days and weeks when Francesca beckoned me to sit down, adding that her husband Graham would fill in as much detail as possible.

Graham was a postie, delivering the mail out of Wiveliscombe. His early morning round with much of it completed before first light in wintertime, would take him through the steeply rising lanes lined with high hedgerows, and eventually to the remotest and barren hill-country. Many deliveries were to the outlying farms and cottages of the Brendon Hills. Some homes nestled in the more sheltered valleys and coombes, while others stood firm against the elements on the high moors that stretched westward to Exmoor and beyond.

I discovered he also had a passionate interest in hawks and owls, hence the aviaries in the garden. He was particularly involved with the breeding of barn owls, and the subsequent controlled release of the youngsters under licence into the wild. He had conducted considerable research locally into the feasibility of the owl chicks' long-term survival and hopefully, of their eventual recovery as breeding adults in areas nearby where barn owls had become absent.

He described many disaster stories of families of youngsters being released in related groups, with no chance to establish territories, and where no studies had been carried out to discover the amount of suitable prey species. Graham's efforts had been much more conscientious, as indeed were the keeping of his birds. The laws governing the release of owls had recently been amended and he was now one of the few people nationwide to be granted a licence to carry out such work by the Department of the Environment. To keep his birds in tip-top condition by providing extra protein in their diet, he would keep an eye open on his rounds for road casualties, particularly small rabbits. Therefore he always had his 'bunny bag' in the van to collect the more unfortunate victims which had come to grief during the previous night.

Yesterday morning had been no different. There in the headlights, and not for the first occasion since leaving the depot, Graham had stopped to pick up a wet and wretched body. But to his amazement as he approached this particular individual there was, in the bright light, a feeble movement from the bedraggled and very cold creature.

Immediately Graham realised he was giving comfort not to yet another rabbit but to something that was so very different from anything he had ever held before. This was no rabbit for sure, but could it possibly be a mink? As he held it very close in the bright headlights, was it perhaps an otter? He was not sure, but through his deep interest and extensive knowledge of the local natural history, he knew that otters had been spotted in the vicinity, and more often than not close to Clatworthy and Wimbleball reservoirs.

As he made the tiny creature as comfortable as possible on the front passenger seat, he realised that if indeed it was an otter cub, he was at that very moment not a stone's throw from the source of many of those rumours. The deep waters of Wimbleball, menacing and inhospitable, having been whipped up by the recent gales, were just the other side of the hill from where he had stopped.

Graham's reactions had been those of a person with experience of the immediate requirements of any distressed creature. But first he had to make contact with his superiors;

then he had hurried to ensure that the remaining mail was delivered on time, which was both his professional remit and also his personal responsibility. But there was also the equally if not more important need to hasten home and to quickly attempt to re-establish this tiny creature again in a warm and safe, but now artificial haven.

A supply of dried substitute milk, originally on stand-by at the neighbouring farm for orphaned lambs that for various reasons had lost their ewes on the hill was quickly collected, so Francesca could immediately provide the first and vital nourishment. Graham had also commenced what turned out initially to be a string of fruitless telephone calls to the more obvious organisations on how best to rear what was appearing ever more likely to the Burrows to be an otter cub. The singular lack of information and enthusiasm for Graham's concern had, quite rightly, disillusioned him.

However, more importantly, Francesca had made the breakthrough. She had persuaded the tiny creature to accept very small amounts of the milk substitute, and significantly the cub's body temperature was beginning to return to something approaching normal. It was evident that the cub had suffered a very close call given the extreme wet weather and cold temperatures of the previous night. Eventually very late that first evening, and following an earlier successful phone call to the Otter Trust headquarters at Earsham, near Bungay in Suffolk, a frustrated Graham had finally made contact with Ken Hill, in north Cornwall. Ken is the manager of the Trust's Tamar Otter Sanctuary which had been opened at North Petherwin, near Launceston in 1986.

Helen and I had known Ken for some considerable time. He had worked for the naturalist Philip Wayre for many years and had decided to move from his native north Norfolk to the totally contrasting environment of a secluded wooded valley in north Cornwall. This was somewhat surprising to me since Ken loved the wide Norfolk landscapes and the profusion of wildfowl and waders to be found on the coastal marshes close to his Corpusty home. The Tamar Otter Sanctuary is boarded by the Boleswater brook, a tributary of the River Ottery, which in turn leads to the rich and rolling farmlands of the Tamar valley and thence to the sea. Under Ken's guidance the British otters there, both bitches Wensum and Tavy, with their accompanying dog Taw, had bred unbelievably well. Many cubs were regularly being returned to

East Anglia to be further acclimatised for the Trust's release programme.

I gathered from Graham that it was indeed Ken who had finally put his mind at rest, confirming that Helen and I would be able to help and that we possessed the only privately owned family group of British otters in the United Kingdom. Quite understandably, Graham and Francesca had tired of the negative and unhelpful advice they had received throughout the first fateful day, and that is why they had waited until the following morning for one final phone call to our home as they attempted to seek the help they needed.

Graham had concluded his description of events; Francesca was continuing to try and coax the cub to accept more of the milk substitute and I felt it was then time to offer my thoughts.

I explained how I felt that it would be advantageous if the cub was quickly in a situation where if it pulled through, it would be close to other otters as it matured. At the same time I warned against any over-optimism of its survival. I recalled Philip Wayre's description of the key stages in the survival of any animal or bird after an injury. There would be three crisis points to be overcome. First there would be an apparent immediate recovery for seventy-two hours. Then there could be two more possible relapses when unforeseen problems might occur at three weeks, and finally after three months. I also pointed out that a licence would have to be quickly obtained from English Nature's headquarters in Peterborough in order to retain the cub since otters were clearly classified as an endangered species. In fact several bodies, including the Licensing Section of the Department of Environment, whose offices were at Tollgate House in Bristol, would need to be informed of the cub's whereabouts, and of any plans being made for its future.

We agreed that on my return home, I would immediately speak with Philip Wayre, the chairman of the Otter Trust. In all probability it was likely to be best if the rearing of the cub was carried out in association with us. Graham and Francesca were clearly disappointed; already in thirty six hours they had forged an unmistakable bond with the cub. Since the unexpected rescue by Graham they had coped with their task in such a caring way that any parting now was going to come hard.

So that's how the situation was left as I took one last and lingering look at the forlorn little creature. In the gathering dusk I parted Hellings Cottages high in the Brendon Hills ; I hoped that

Francesca's kindness and patience would not be wasted. But in the bottom of my heart I felt it was going to be touch and go.

Darkness had indeed closed in rapidly and now I had to concentrate hard as I found my way through the first few miles of remote lanes towards Wellington, and eventually my return journey to Old Holt Farm.

I could not really believe what I had just seen; this was only my second 'wild' otter cub in over twenty-five years: What had really happened to cause this cub to be abandoned, to become separated and lost from her immediate family before first light? Would I ever discover the truth, or indeed would she survive what must have been, and still was, an ongoing traumatic period for her. I did not want these questions to remain unsolved. But little did I realise as I continually searched in the darkness of the winter's night for the correct turnings that I was eventually going to have a relationship with this orphan which would lead me to discovering many of the answers.

Just now though, I was in a state of high excitement and uncertain what to do next. A short while later I was back in Wellington with the motorway connection to the M5 north no more than five minutes drive away. I relaxed and again my mind strayed Here I was actively pursuing my commitment to wildlife conservation, which had grown and by necessity had changed constantly in direction over the many years and I was in the town where, outside of my closest family, one of the people most responsible for my present predicament had both recently lived and worked. When I was at school at Clifton College in Bristol, John Kendall-Carpenter was master in charge of rugby. He was a Cornishman who played for Penzance and Newlyn, Bath, Oxford University and England. He had captained both Oxford and England. As I trained and played as a junior colt, I used to regularly watch 'Kendall' training the school's first XV during the week, before he left to play at weekends for his country in the Home Nations Championship. I used to watch those matches with my father and school friends on our black and white television set.

Rugby was very important to me at Clifton and I was to make the XV relatively quickly, captaining the school in my third year in the side. Kendall was a most effective coach and adviser on the rugby field but he was also a true friend, a master who both listened to, and took a genuine interest in, those who were around him. His work for and interest in the pupil was not confined to school hours. On more than one occasion he had listened to me either on the train or coach travelling to away matches, enthusing about my collection of wild ducks and geese which lived on the ponds we had built in the back garden of my home, and about the enjoyment they were giving to my family and friends. He had realised from those conversations that the academic courses I was following were not going to give me the relevant standards at 'A' level for the chance of a subsequent university place. A brief conversation with my parents on the touchline after a match against Blundell's School near Tiverton in Devon resulted in a dramatic change of course.

By harnessing my already burgeoning interest both in wildlife and in the places where they live to a more practical approach to my 'A' level studies, I was able to obtain results which gave me possible entry to either Oxford or Cambridge universities as a realistic goal. I read Geography at Pembroke College, Cambridge for three years. But after leaving school with that potential course still ahead of me, I had a two year break. This gave me the opportunity to work with the naturalist Philip Wayre at his then home in Norfolk. I was to learn hugely from my work and experiences with him and all sorts of seeds were sown in my mind before even going up to Cambridge. So thanks to my rugby coach showing more than a passing interest in what was an already consuming hobby at the age of sixteen, university studies, wildlife conservation and rugby were high on my agenda, though I seem to remember they were not necessarily held in that order of priority! Now was the time, on this very occasion when I was actually passing through Wellington close to the public school where Kendall had been headmaster before his premature death, to think again briefly but respectfully of the man. He was, probably, as responsible as any other person for the fact that I was in the area at all that afternoon, and particularly becoming involved in the long-term rescue of an otter cub.

I made three phone calls that evening, as I formulated my plans.

Firstly, I summarised the background of the situation to Philip Wayre and his advice was quite clear.

"It's important," he informed me, "that the cub is quickly established in 'ottery' surroundings."

I explained that Helen and I had a close friend, Wendy Lee, of many years standing, who had a reputation for being successful with all the various young creatures that by chance had come her way over the years. Wendy and her husband Roger lived and worked on Lord Bledisloe's estate at Aylburton close to Lydney in the Royal Forest of Dean.

"With all the commitments to our family group of otters I think she will be far and away the best bet to ensure the cub's survival in the critical first few days. Although she does have a part-time job," I added, "and I have yet to speak to her, I feel sure she will be able to give the time and effort that is going to be essential for success".

"That sounds fine," Philip agreed "and don't forget either to keep the Nature Conservancy Council informed of the cub's whereabouts and progress. Do keep in touch. I know my wife Jeanne will be interested in how the cub progresses too; so good luck and good night."

So the next vital call was across the river Severn. I had turned to Roger and Wendy for help previously. Give Wendy a baby's bottle and the right proprietary brand of substitute milk, Ostermilk No 2 took some beating over the years, and she was in seventh heaven! She had saved and nurtured back to good health young animals as varied as both badger and fox cubs, and fallow and roe deer fawns; there was a magnificent herd of fallow deer roaming free within the parkland of the estate. But by far and away her most successful achievement had been way back in 1983. She had saved a litter of triplet otter cubs in our family group after events had suddenly gone drastically wrong for their mother. However I had removed the youngsters at the first sign of trouble, and the adult bitch happily also survived her ordeal. Wendy brought all three youngsters, two dog cubs and one much smaller bitch cub, to maturity. It had become clear that even before the cubs were removed the female youngster was already losing ground to her dominant brothers. This pattern was to be repeated again in later years with further births involving triplets, although I was unaware on each occassion of the significance of the number of dog cubs in the litter. On that first occasion both male cubs were subsequently gifts to the Otter Trust's release programme; they sired litters on numerous occasions at Earsham and many of their cubs were eventually released to the wild.

"Of course we will help," was Wendy's initial reaction. My conversation continued with her husband Roger who immediately became very excited. His brief questions spilled down the line, each one fired at me before I'd had the chance to answer the previous one.

"Where, and how, and I wonder why," he demanded, "and it's absolutely amazing that it's even alive given the time of year and the recent weather. When will we be seeing you?" he finally concluded.

" I still don't have that much detail," I managed to interrupt at last. "I'll now ring the Burrows and see if I can organise the cub's early collection. Then I will talk to you again soon".

So far, so good, but now came the hardest of the three calls. I had to call up the two people who by their commitment and skill had brought the cub through the first hours of what hopefully would conclude in her full recovery. It was late now, nearly nine o'clock.

"It's David speaking, David Chaffe. I came to see your otter cub this afternoon." I began somewhat tentatively.

"Hello, yes it's Francesca, we were wondering if you would call back tonight".

"I've spoken to Philip Wayre, chairman of the Otter Trust, at his home in Suffolk just a short while ago," I continued, "and have explained the circumstances. He does feel that it would be best for the cub to be taken on by us."

There was a distinct pause.

"Oh," said the voice rather faintly on the other end of the line, and immediately I could sense the feeling of extreme disappointment. "I was hoping, that's to say Graham and I, we were hoping to keep her a little while longer yet; you see, I've managed to get her to take a little more milk tonight."

"That's encouraging," I continued, "but of course there's the additional problem that within forty-eight hours, seventy-two at the most, the relevant authorities will have to be informed of its whereabouts. Since it will be reared on behalf of the Otter Trust, then any possible technical and legal difficulties in that direction could be quickly resolved."

"Oh, I fully realise that, but we've had her for so short a while, and the fact that she's to be moved again, well it seems....." With that, Francesca's voice died away.

Seven years later I can understand her sense of impending loss far more. This otter cub was quickly becoming part of their family; the fight and determination to keep it alive immediately after its sudden and totally unexpected arrival had in a very short space of time overtaken all the other everyday household routines of Graham and Francesca and their young family. I was hoping that Francesca could come to terms with the inevitable fact that the long-term future of the cub lay elsewhere. I can clearly recall the bravery of her next remark.

"What time would you be wanting to collect her" she responded, "and where exactly?"

I was greatly relieved. She had quite unselfishly, although emotionally torn, taken the best option for the cub.

"My immediate plans are that she will continue to be reared on the bottle for as long as is necessary by some close friends of ours who live in the Forest of Dean. I want to deliver her by

Relations of Willow, Islay, Rowan, Houdini, Cider and Blackthorn are still breeding successfully at The Otter Trust's headquarters which are to be found at Earsham, just off the main A143 road, one mile W of Bungay, Suffolk. Telephone 01986 893470.

tomorrow evening so, if it's convenient, maybe we could meet in the car-park of the Goat House, a roadside restaurant on the A38, at Edithmead, close to junction 22 on the M5 heading north. Shall we say two-thirty?"

"Yes alright, we will be there; in the meantime, I'll see how much more milk she'll take throughout the night; so fingers crossed and goodnight for now," Francesca concluded.

I relaxed in my study and realised that stage one of the rescue plan was concluded. But now for tomorrow. It was vital to settle the cub in her new environment as quickly as possible. It was most important in order to secure her survival, that she regularly took an increased amount of milk at each feed. Every four hours or so would be best without going to the other extreme of overfeeding her. I was going to rely on Wendy's expertise to see us over that hurdle. However I still could not dismiss her disproportionate shape and the listless staring coat; I was once involved in the rescue of a common seal pup and that too was all head and shoulders with a skeletal body. We pumped the pup full of a highly rich milk substitute, enriched with vitamin oils akin to

those of it's mother's milk and yet still that pup succumbed. So yes, I was tense and nervous about the eventual outcome, even though the Burrows had done their very best for her so far.

In bed I explained my anxieties to Helen, and much earlier when I had seen Olivia off to sleep, I explained to her that we were likely to become very closely involved with an abandoned otter cub. Naturally I did not disclose to her that I thought there was no more than a fifty per cent chance, if that, of her survival. However this little bitch cub was to turn out to be a real fighter. I hoped she might take a little more milk that night, and continue to reap the benefits of being really warm again. I trusted lady luck would go with her and that the possibility of a chill, caught when exposed before she was rescued, and which would inevitably lead to pneumonia, would not materialise.

All otters need their fair share of luck I thought to myself, as finally Helen put out the lights.

Our meeting with the Burrows next afternoon was understandably emotional but necessarily brief. The cub was quickly transferred into a small box with her existing bedding. To this was added another motley assortment of my well worn and discarded sweaters, plus a hot water bottle. Francesca confirmed that she had indeed taken a little more milk, four ounces now since being retrieved from the lane. As I felt her gently, her body temperature seemed fair and there were no obvious signs of scouring which would have given cause for considerable concern.

I explained to Graham and Francesca that if the cub progressed and survived that they would be most welcome to visit her whenever in the Forest of Dean, and similarly if her recovery proved to be long-term, to come to our home.

There was obvious sadness by my hurried departure; the thanks Helen and I conveyed could not and did not I feel now, do justice to the forty-eight hours of total commitment that Graham and Francesca had given to the victim of a rough winter's night.

Soon I was speeding on, northbound on the M5 towards Bristol and the crossing into Wales via the Severn Bridge . The Burrows would be returning southbound on the same motorway to their cottage in the Brendon Hills. But now they would be returning to an empty house, their lives touched permanently no doubt, by the extremely rare phenomenon for most families of briefly having an otter cub in their midst.

The next vital episode in the cub's brief life was about to begin.

Very soon I was past the first of the key landmarks of my journey. The tidal creek of the Yeo river meanders gently through the flat marshy fields of Kingston Seymour and then it stretches further away to the Severn Estuary to the west. The flocks of grazing sheep, brought in their thousands to the milder climes of the West Country from the hills of northern England and the Scottish Borders, were grazing very determinedly in the fitful winter sunshine. The gales and heavy rain of the past few days were being rapidly replaced by colder brighter weather. although the end result of the persistent downpours were the water filled ruts in the fields and their gateways. This was a land where otters use the drainage ditches and the main river to move from the estuary in winter to the nearby Mendip Hills in summer. As elsewhere they had become rare but signs of a slow recovery were becoming apparent. Occasional sightings had been reported to me; a brief conversation from a public telephone box late one afternoon with an excited lady caller from Exeter Bus Station went something like this:

"Is that Mr David Chaffe?" started the slightly frantic voice.

"Yes. who's calling?"

"You are the otter man aren't you. only I have just come down the M5 through north Somerset where you live. and not an hour ago I saw an otter, or at least I think it was an otter. It was. well it was like a large cat lying on its back grooming its tummy."

"What colour was it?" I managed to interrupt briefly.

"It was dark brown.... It was obviously wet. It was down below me as we were speeding past. stretched out on the bank in the sun."

"Sounds very like an otter." I continued.

"Oh drat!. there go the pips. Anyway I thought you'd be interested. Good-bye."

With that the excited voice was gone; I recalled it was wintertime; obviously it was a dog otter enjoying an afternoon siesta and a lazy groom in the last warmth of the winter sun, probably after a good lunch of Severn eel.

Sadly not every report was to be as positive. Closer to Clevedon another adult dog otter. four feet long from tip of nose to tip of tail, had been killed before first light, knocked down and run over by a milk tanker not far from the hamlet at Kenn. He had lost his life as he slipped over the road bridge above the sluice gates just at the point where the tidal flow of the Kenn river meets the freshwaters of the Nailsea moors.

As I remembered the unnecessary loss of that otter, I immediately glanced across and downwards. I had placed the box holding the cub in the footwell of the van on the front passenger's side. The cub was still well covered in the varied assortment of old clothing, with only her muzzle showing and she appeared to be sleeping peacefully.

I travelled on, with the motorway climbing the Cadbury ridge. In no time the Gordano Levels were below me to the west, and easily visible from the two-tiered motorway. The occasional tumbledown field barn, and the wet fields with their countless pollarded willows lining reed fringed ditches were still the haunt of barn and little owls, and of grey herons. However the summer-visiting reed warblers were long departed and would presently be in warm west Africa. Sadly the Gordano valley was another area where the rich wild flower pastures were being increasingly destroyed by systematic drainage, courtesy of grants and subsidies. So sadly lapwing and snipe no longer bred, although happily the wintering short-eared owls would still be quartering the area later that afternoon.

From Gordano I looked for my first views of Portbury Wharf where nearly forty years ago my father used to take me on unforgettable bird-watching trips. They meant long walks from the end of the metalled lane until we reached the sea-bank; we skirted deep ditches where thick hawthorn hedges hung over the water enabling countless moorhens to hide. What surprises awaited me. My first wild geese, European whitefronts, a family group away from the thousands of the main flock thirty miles upstream at Slimbridge; also my first barn owl, ghost-like and suddenly floating out of the sea-mist in front of us late one November afternoon. But the highlight was spending many evenings one summer lying hidden under a khaki blanket. With the singing skylarks high above, we closed in on and then photographed the nest and eggs of a redshank. We would have one parent redshank under close scrutiny as it returned to the exact tuft where its partner was hidden. Then an ever-watchful male shelduck, whose nesting female was on her eggs deep in the rabbit burrows of the adjacent sea defences, would spot us. His strident and distinctive alarm calls promptly warned all and sundry across the summer grazing pastures. With our redshanks now on red alert for the next couple of hours or so, we would dejectedly retrace our footsteps to plan another attempt on a different occasion.

Whenever possible I always left the M5 at junction 18 to take the coast road to the Severn Bridge. After leaving school and before going to Norfolk, I had worked briefly for the main contractors on a major road scheme, the Filton by-pass substitute, which would eventually become part of the M5. From my field caravan I tested soil types and stone aggregates. The first Severn Bridge was then under active construction too, and there was much liaison between the companies involved. I soon began to know well the 'Severnside' route, through Avonmouth, past ICI Severnside and Pilning, and eventually through to Aust and the Bridge. The meadows and creeks close to the estuary shore were little different from those alongside the River Kenn further downstream. Yet another of those phone calls but this time in late autumn, reported a bitch otter with two half-grown cubs at foot playing at low water in a pill, a local term for a tidal creek, in the broad daylight of mid-afternoon.

Some people were always in the right place at the right time!

Traffic levels were now far higher than predicted when construction of the bridge was completed some twenty-five years previously and the high level of corrosion of the superstructure caused by the toxic elements spewing forth into the atmosphere from the chemical complexes of Avonmouth and carried upstream by the predominantly westerly winds had not been anticipated. So plans for the Second Severn Crossing had already been announced, and this time the new crossing was to follow the route of Brunel's Great Western Railway tunnel, which had been widely predicted as the first choice for the existing bridge. It would use for its base the stratas of rocks leading to the English Stones where, at the lowest of spring tides, they are exposed to view right across the estuary leaving only the narrowest of deep water channels, called The Shutes, close to the Welsh bank. It was at this point that the Romans had forded the river during the periods of slack water, as no doubt have the local Severn otters over generations. Well before low water, the otters, as did the legionnaires, make use of The Bull, a large upright stone and also of a ridge of rocks called The Goslin Ledge, as vantage points. I had previously received several reports of sightings in that area, indicating a possible breeding holt nearby on the Welsh bank where the overspill waters of a lake join the estuary not far upstream.

The alternate lack of movement of my vehicle as I waited for the long queue to move forward, followed by the frequent stop-go as I approached the requisite toll-booth at the approach to the bridge crossing, caused the cub to stir. As I pulled away she seemed to come out of her deep sleep. There was a tenseness and nervousness about her. For the first time I could detect fear in her eyes. By the time I had slowly crossed the bridge in single file because of the ongoing repairs and strengthening works, her apprehension had become noticeably more pronounced. I wanted to reassure her but decided to wait until I had completed the secondary crossing of the river Wye and was clear of Chepstow. Then I took the plunge.

"So how did you come to find yourself in this mess?" I started gently.

The tiny cub looked at me with some despair. I could see she was very weak, but I felt she desperately wanted to respond.

"You're going to be alright now," I continued so as to reassure her. "I am your Dad and I am taking you to meet two very close friends who are going to look after you for a while; Wendy, that's the lady's name, she will feed you plenty of milk to help you recover and grow. She'll make sure you stay very warm. You won't get cold again; she'll play with you, and show you some of the things your real mummy was already teaching you. When you're feeling much stronger and eating well for yourself, you'll come to live with me, and my wife Helen and our daughter Olivia. Olivia will play with you too, and you will live with other otters, and we'll all be friends together. How about that?"

"Won't I ever see my mummy again?" she whispered.

"Sadly I don't think so, but I am sure she never intended to lose you. Can you remember what happened? Do you remember being found and being picked up when it was still dark?"

"Everything was fine up to a few days ago," the cub continued. "We were in our holt all cosy and dry."

"Who's we?" I interrupted quietly.

"Me and my two brothers. Mum was with us most of the time, she'd only go out occasionally to feed. My problem was that my brothers used to push in very hard to suckle mum's milk. They were a right couple of bullies and I often used to miss out. I became very hungry at times; it seemed to me that she favoured them. However in the end I always got some milk and at least I always managed to snuggle under her tummy and stay warm."

The little cub was now in full flow, and I decided not to interrupt her but to gather as much information as I could about recent events.

"Then last weekend, on the Saturday, there was a terrible commotion not far away. We could hear people shouting and the sound of vehicles and of horses hooves close by. Mum was gone, just like that, presumably to see what all the fuss was about. She was away a very long time. We were very frightened so we stayed still, huddled together, and this time my brothers allowed me to stay close to them. We all kept very quiet as mum had told us to do whenever we were on our own. We just waited. It seemed an age, and when eventually she came home I could see she was really upset."

The cub was spilling out her story in great detail now; I could sense she was reliving the awful last few days. It was as if she had relapsed suddenly into a state of shock, and there was obviously far more to come yet. I decided to coax the cub on with her story.

"Did your mum tell you what she had seen?"

"For a long while she said nothing. She was really restless, whickering at us all the time to keep still and quiet. She didnt even seem to have the inclination to allow us to feed. But then, yes, she came out with it. You see, the people and the horses, they were part of the hunt. She'd gone out to see how close they were to our home, our holt. But they were really after the local foxes. What mum didn't realise was that when she first came across the gathering, the huntsmen and the horses had only just started to gather. She said she had ended up by mistake on the wrong side of them and therefore further away from our holt. So when yet more dogs, horses and people continued to arrive there was no way she could get back to us without giving herself away. Then finally, before the hunt set off, a small group of hounds somehow picked up her scent so she had to slip quickly and quietly into the river and move upstream. So then she was even further away from us. She decided to wait several hours before risking coming home along another of her regular routes. But at the foot of the bridge where she wanted to cut across the river to reach us she discovered the last of the horse boxes were still being loaded. It was nearly dark now and she had been gone nearly all day. She was really exhausted."

I was now about half-way to my destination after leaving the bridge on the Welsh side, and it was clear that I had heard only part of the story.

"Mum stayed in all day Sunday, she was that frightened. It wasn't until after a good night's sleep that very early on the Monday morning she was away again quite suddenly, saying that she needed to feed. I was pretty hungry too, I can tell you. Although mum had slept well, we'd had two bad nights. She wasn't prepared to suckle us, and my brothers were now equally hungry and were really getting very stroppy and bad tempered. To our surprise mum was back quite quickly, around mid-morning. We had expected her to be gone much longer. It was raining very hard indeed, and to make matters worse there was a really strong gale blowing. All we could hear was the noise of the wind in the trees, the sound of the river nearby rushing past and the branches of the trees creaking and groaning. That was when mum told us."

"Told you what?" I really did not need to ask, for the cub was going to finish her story.

"Mum said if the rain didn't stop soon, she was going to abandon our holt, and take us to another she had already organised not that far away. She said that her own mother, our granny, had moved home when she was a cub of about six weeks of age. Mum said about not staying in one place for too long, something about never knowing who may have come to know of the holt's whereabouts, because of us noisy cubs, and especially because of my brothers who were always squabbling. Also, she was really frightened that the huntsmen who had called in the breakaway group of hounds might have guessed from the dogs' reactions that they had discovered another animal's scent and droppings, the spraints of an otter.

She was also back from her evening feed far more quickly than usual. It still hadn't stopped raining either, so she was now worried about the rising river level. She would always go to the nearby warren for the young rabbits whenever she wanted food quickly. The rabbit family had gone. The wrens that lived in the thickets nearby and whose chattering acted as a warning system were suddenly no longer around either, and I think she was convinced that by now all our neighbours had already taken the necessary precautions. She then told us that if it didn't stop raining during the night, we would all be in the new holt by first light. During the evening the rain never let up. I could tell she was disturbed. She was continually turning herself around us, drawing us ever closer into her warm body one moment, then constantly breaking away to go to the holt's entrance. She was becoming increasingly fretful, and my brothers even started complaining that she wouldn't stay in one place long enough for them to finish a feed. 'Now you know what it's like to go hungry', I told them, 'and often I don't get any milk at all'. At that stage Mum told us to stop quarrelling. But eventually she seemed to settle down with us all very tight into the soft fur of her tummy.

We must have all dropped off to sleep because the next thing I remember I was being vigorously shaken and woken up. I heard Mum saying, 'well, which one of you is coming first, and who's staying. I'll be back shortly', she added, and with that she was gone from the holt having grabbed one of my brothers in her mouth. It seemed an age before she was back; she was very wet and promptly snapped at my other brother. 'Get a move on,' she screamed, 'everything is taking an age, the weather out there is atrocious' and with that she grabbed him in the same way. But just before she did so, she'd told me to stay exactly where I was. When they had disappeared I was very lonely and frightened. There were no other sounds than the falling rain and the roar of the wind in the trees."

"Did she return for you?" I interrupted. I was intrigued. Was this the moment of the unplanned separation?

"Oh yes, I didn't think she was going to come back, but in fact she was much quicker than the time before."

"So how did you come to be lost then?" I was even more puzzled now.

"Mum carried me just as she did my brothers as she stretched out of our holt. She first had to climb a very steep and slippery wet bank but eventually she managed it. Then she made her way under some alder and willow trees which were bending and creaking in the gale. Mum then suddenly stopped, put me down and told me that directly above us and on the other side of a lane was our new holt. It was on higher ground, much drier and no way would it become flooded. The only problem was that we would be further away from the safety of the river. She told me to stay where I was, and I thought, of course, she had gone to check her route. But when she returned just a few moments later, she appeared quite annoyed again. 'What's the matter now,' I said, 'can't we go on?' I'd never been outside the holt before, and I was very frightened.

"Yes, we can alright. But unfortunately on the way back to fetch you a barn owl has appeared. This last summer the adult birds that live in and around the farm buildings which are not far from the holt where you were born, reared three chicks. I don't know what became of two of the youngsters but the third individual, a young male, still lives with his parents. He obviously first spotted me first when I was taking your brother on the last trip, but now he has started making an awful racket. Goodness knows what he's doing out in this weather. He should be asleep like all other sensible creatures on a night like this. To be honest he's not a very pleasant character either, bossy and very cocky; he thinks he can do no wrong. I know he sets out to aggravate the rabbits," she continued. "Do you know at dusk and dawn when he's out hunting he just drifts in and out on them, teasing the youngsters whilst they're grazing. They're far too big for him to take anyway but he does it simply to annoy and frighten them."

"Mum was really worked up about this owl. As she came back for me he was still high up in a large willow tree bobbing and weaving his head in the pouring rain."

"I don't suppose he'll attack us, he'll just make a song and dance as usual about us being close to his territory, or to be more accurate his parents' territory. I am surprised his father still tolerates him around," Mum continued angrily.

"I asked her if we were going or not, and she said we would have to take a chance. She said she couldn't leave my brothers any longer and she couldn't also leave me where I was. Although it wasn't going to be light yet for a couple of hours, Mum said that vehicles would soon be in and out of the nearby farm as the early morning milking of the dairy herd would begin before first light. She had been close to that area for so long now she knew all the movements and timings of the animals and of the people who looked after them. Mum waited no longer and grabbed me by the scruff of my neck. I can remember going through some very wet long grass and rushes and I could feel the cold stems bending past me. Obviously I thought mum knew exactly where she was, after all it was her territory. Then suddenly she stopped yet again and put me down."

"I'll just reach up over the bank here and check where I am," she said, "I need to cross the lane at this point, otherwise we shall be going further and further away from our new holt. We should be beyond that barn owl by now, and I have marked this lower route across the meadows several times before. Although it has been raining very hard, I should still be able to pick up my scent."

Moments later she was back; "quick," she said, "I think he's gone. Let's go. With that she lifted me up and started to climb the bank towards the lane."

"But if you were nearly there and the owl had gone," I started, "then surely...." but before I could continue the cub carried on with her story. It was as if she was letting go the anguish of her parting from her mother.

"We were in the lane." The cub paused, then continued "Well all I can remember was a blinding flash of white. The owl came from nowhere and launched himself straight at us. I can still feel his soft feathers because for a moment his wings seemed to envelop us. I heard mum scream out in pain. I think he must have dug his talons into her face as he swooped in on us. The next thing I knew he was gone, but Mum had vanished as well. She had dropped me in the lane. I did not know what to do. I thought she'd come back for me and I also hoped the owl would not come back. I just stayed still. Mum always told us to do that if we were frightened or heard something strange close to the holt."

"So how long did you stay there?"

"Well not for long. I was cold and getting very wet. I was sure she would appear at any moment. But she never did. So I decided to go back down the bank and wait. I thought Mum might pick up her scenting places and retrace her route to our old holt. But after waiting for a while I panicked, and decided to go across the lane in the general direction we had been heading, hoping all the time that the owl would by now have gone away. But just at that moment there was a roaring noise. I had never heard anything like that before and then there was silence."

"That was the noise of a vehicle's engine, which was then switched off, hence everything going quiet," I interrupted.

"Well whatever it was, the next thing I remember was being lifted out of the lane; I was placed on something soft and thoroughly smelly, in fact all the smells were new and strange. But at least it was warmer, and by now I was quite numb with the cold. Do you know, I remember nothing after that until I felt some warm liquid in my mouth. I was being held again, but the hands and fingers were less rough, much softer in fact, and warmer too; and there was a totally different scent about them."

"That was Francesca trying to persuade you to accept some artificial milk," I said, "she was planning to make you feel better and I expect by then your body must have already felt warmer too."

"Oh, I was far less cold but still very hungry; in fact, I am hungry right now. With my brothers pushing and shoving me around, I only occasionally had my share of mum's milk. I had also been trying to sleep a lot, I always felt tired and exhausted but at least I was warm . Last night after I had drunk some more of that other milk out of the bottle, I think I heard the lady talking to you. Are you David?"

"That's right," I replied, "I am David, and I am taking you to live for a while with Roger and Wendy; you'll enjoy being with her, she's looked after tiny creatures before. She'll make you better. Then when you feel you can eat solid food, meat and fish......"

"Mum used to tell us about the various animals and birds she used to catch," interrupted the cub.

"Well when you can do that you will be coming to live with us. That's Helen, my wife, and our daughter Olivia, she's five now; I expect you will enjoy playing with her and she with you. I told her before she went to school this morning about collecting you, and taking you temporarily to a new home. In fact, it won't be long before we are there now."

I slowed over the railway lines that cross the main street of Lydney. The van vibrated as we crossed the now redundant single track that used to carry freight to and from Lydney docks on the west bank of the Severn estuary deep into the Forest of Dean at Parkend.

I glanced back into the box, expecting the cub's frantic conversation of the last few miles to continue but clearly she had become suddenly very drowsy. A desperate feeling came over me as I looked at her and realised again how weak she really was; indeed having changed her position to go to sleep, how small she appeared. She was also very thin, and although her coat was dry, it stared at you. I began to feel nervous about her survival after her traumatic few days. It was not so much that she had become lost, but rather that previously she had so regularly lost out to her brothers on her share of her mother's nourishing milk. Together those circumstances might just prove too big a hurdle for her to overcome.

Anxiously I pressed on over the few final miles. From the A48 road to Gloucester I climbed steeply towards Viney Hill and the Forest. In the van's headlights I picked out the forest's sheep, huddled in their twos and threes close to the road amongst the best of the remaining winter cover of the 'commons'. It was still raining hard, and in fact as the road climbed ever higher the rain was quickly changing into wet sleet. The weather would be no different on the Brendon Hills and Exmoor tonight; both would be as equally exposed to the elements as the Forest. My thoughts were now of the cub's mother and the cub's two sibling brothers; hopefully they were well established again, safe and dry in their new holt.

A sharp left hand turn took me down a dark lane, and the lights of a remote cottage were suddenly welcoming me to my destination. The cub had arrived.

I first met Frank Owen, keeper of the Teifi Pools in mid-Wales, in the late 1950s. This led to many expeditions searching for otters, or at least for signs of them, around the Tregaron Bog.

*ter had been found as a cub at the top of the tide on Salthouse Marsh, North Norfolk, on Boxing Day 1966.

© Ian Anderson

My first otter cub. In the early 1980s I became only the second person in the last hundred years to have bred the British otter.

The same cub, half-grown, and still with her mother

'Do you remember those triplets we saved for you all those years ago?' (1982)

'Then, the little bitch cub needed all Wendy's attention to pull her through...'

© Ian Anderson

One of my early dog otters who fathered several cubs.

© Ian Anderson

Another successful breeding pair,
dog and bitch otter and their
single female cub (top left).

Another of the successful breeding bitches

Jim Hale

My first book, 'And Let the Earth Listen' complimented the creation of my Wildlife Park and my accompanying lecturing programme for schools.
Morag, a hand-reared sow badger.

...and Dick, a hand-reared orphaned common seal, who was on indefinite loan from Ronald Lockley.

Presenting Wildlife 'Face-to-Face' to parents and their youngsters at St Martin's C of E School, Worle, North Somerset.

Mandy Williams and Caroline Woodley, both aged 10, from Wembdon, near Bridgwater, at Somerset Wildlife Trust's HQ in early 1981, getting to know Gonzo, one of my European eagle owls.

Later with many other children, they would have met my tame vixen foxes, Razzle and Rusty.

Somerset schoolgirl Dora Westlake, aged 14, won the regional section in the senior category of the Young Environmentalist of the Year Award. Storm was also invited to Dora's presentation ceremony!

Storm at Stogursey Primary Scool in West Somerset, being introduced to Lewis Winter and Kelly Touchin and before being presented to parents to boost the school's restoration appeal.

Storm at her favourite lecture venue, Hinkley Point Visitor Centre, this time with Spaxton chool pupils James Heal, Emily Bennett and Kezia Wilson. The asic message from my lectures as, and still is, quite simple: to urvive, the otter needs the same hree conditions as humans – a secure home, a supply of food and clean water. It's all rather ike getting people to wear seat belts – you have to repeat the message over and over again.

Whenever at Hinkley, Storm is close to where her wild mother may well have made er way onto Exmoor via one of the many streams that flow into the Bristol Channel close to the nuclear power station.

© Finnbarr Webster. Copy ·Joanna Quinn, courtesy
Dorset Evening Echo

*Storm still presenting her conservation
message in the spring of '99 to the Dorset
Otter Group at Frampton Village Hall near
Dorchester. "It is not often you can stand
in a hall packed with more than one
hundred very excited people and it's so
quiet that you can hear a pin drop."*

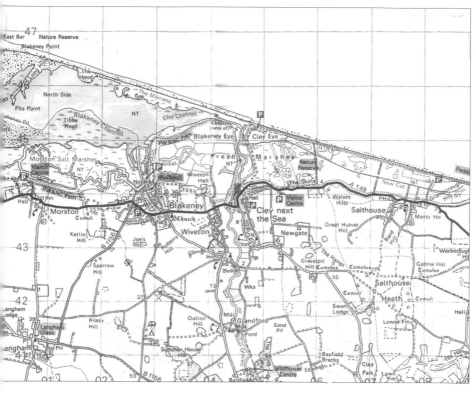

North Norfolk

'Bob and Joan's cottage would be eventually found at the far end of the
magnificent blanket of coastal marsh and reclaimed fields that lie behind
the shingle ridge at Salthouse.'

FIVE

"SHE'S CLEARLY OLDER THAN SHE LOOKS"

"You've made good time," announced Wendy as she opened the front door of the cottage, "It's a nasty old night out there. Helen phoned just after you left Somerset so I had a rough time of your arrival."

I was standing in the outer porch of the cottage from where I could already appreciate the warmth of the adjacent kitchen, and the strong aromas from the evening meal cooking on the Aga stove. Both were very welcome on this bitter February night high up in the Forest.

"Well, where is she?" demanded Wendy impatiently.

"I'll fetch her from the van," I replied. "Are you ready to feed her?"

"Yes, let's get started straight away. I collected the Ostermilk from Lydney earlier; I just have to bring it to the right temperature and then I'll see what she will take."

Quickly back indoors again, I waited anxiously for Wendy's initial reaction. She had many years experience of various waifs and strays that had come her way, most of which she had then successfully reared to maturity.

"She looks a poor little mite" was her initial reaction, "and pretty thin too. Do you have any idea what might have happened to her?"

"We shall be lucky if we ever know that," I replied, for at that moment I was not ready to confide the cub's story. "The best thing we can do for her," I continued, "is to persuade her to take some milk, make her warm and keep our fingers crossed that she hasn't caught a chill."

"Absolutely."

Wendy dripped the Ostermilk onto the back of her hand to test for the right temperature and carefully lifted the cub into her lap from the mêleé of sweaters. She immediately showed her experience and technique in bottle-feeding as she quickly inserted the teat, which she had previously softened by boiling, into the cub's mouth. I could see that the angle of the babies bottle was right, for within moments the cub was suckling, and strongly too!

"There we go then, that wasn't too difficult, was it?" smiled Wendy.

I watched quietly, and was more relieved as every minute passed. Suddenly there was a crash as the front door sprang open. Roger was home; within seconds his tall frame was enveloping the armchair, Wendy and the cub.

"How's it doing, Sal,?" (his name of endearment for Wendy after many years of marriage.)

Wendy gently withdrew the teat from the cub's mouth.

"Astonishingly she's just taken three ounces in the last ten minutes."

"Hold on Sal," cautioned Roger, "you know we'll have to be careful against giving her too much too quickly. You could bloat her with dire consequences especially if she hasn't had much milk for some time. But even so, that's pretty good going."

I explained that she had taken about four ounces during the past thirty-six hours, but how much she had received from her mother in the days beforehand was debatable. However, she had been warm and dry at the Burrows and had regained her body temperature after being picked up extremely cold and wet. We agreed that for the moment there was no more that could be done; we would hope that from now on, prompted by Wendy, she would feed consistently and regularly.

A little later over supper we shared the details of my recent ottery news. Then it was time for me to travel home. I drew a couple of sweaters gently around the cub and my last glance saw her sleeping peacefully, very still except for the occasional twitch of a muscle. I tried to convince myself that I would see her alive again; I desperately hoped that she would still be with us in a few days time when I was planning to return with Helen and Olivia.

"Don't you worry," Wendy interrupted my thoughts. "we'll be doing our best. I'll be feeding again in two or three hours."

"Can I ring you later tonight to see how things go at that feed?"

"Of course."

I gave Roger and Wendy the extra supplies of Ostermilk that Helen had purchased before the afternoon rendezvous in Somerset, and which I hoped would be needed. With that I bade farewell to my friends. As I crossed the lane to my vehicle I was distracted by a small flock of ewes taking shelter. Huddled tightly together against the wall of the cottage, they were seeking as much respite as possible from the worst of the winter storm.

During the journey home my mind was filled with the picture of this forlorn little cub, so vulnerable and alone amongst the makeshift and strange artificial bedding and importantly away from the familiar sounds and smells of her mother and siblings. The more I thought of the circumstances leading to her discovery, the more I convinced myself she would not survive. The events of the previous seventy-two hours and the long-term loss of good nutrition would surely prove too great a handicap.

I worried about her mother and two brothers. There had been no let-up in the poor weather and the long-range forecast would be offering little respite for the bitch otter. Had her decision to move to the alternative holt been a success? Would she put herself and her young at risk if she continually went back to look for her lost cub? She would never know that she had now been rescued in the lane where the barn owl had attacked. I trusted that the bitch's wild instincts would remind her to concentrate on what she had, her two boys, and not on what might have been. I became more despondent about my cub and further frustrated as I realised I would probably never know the answers to the outcome of her wild relations.

Home at last, Helen did her best to paint a brighter and more hopeful picture, but I knew because of our shared experiences over many years that she had her doubts too.

Now it was time again to contact the Lees. I waited anxiously for my call to be answered. The phone seemed to be ringing for an age and I could feel my heart pumping.

"She's taken another three ounces, not twenty minutes ago," Roger announced.

"That's great news," I responded excitedly. "Roger, can I ring you tomorrow, say early evening."

"We're not out of the woods yet you know," he added.

"But," I interrupted.

"No, you listen," he interrupted me, "we're on our way, maybe. I'll be home from work at the same time. Talk to you then."

I remember telling Helen more about my trip over the Severn as we prepared for bed. But I do not remember going off to sleep.

Inevitably the next day passed very slowly. Obviously I thought of the cub and her well-being, as I rather methodically and almost from memory fed the other otters already in our family group. I dwelled particularly on the bitches, trying to imagine which one the cub would resemble most, if she survived to maturity. But inevitably my mind drifted to the fact that there was a wild otter cub not far away, fighting for its life and needing all the luck going.

During the day I took time to provide both the Nature Conservancy Council, now English Nature, and The Department of the Environment, with the 'up to date' information and whereabouts of the cub. I gave fresh dry bedding to all our otters to protect them against the elements before finally feeding the group as dusk approached. By now Helen would have brought Olivia home from school, so it was time to go and share Olivia's news, which was always a most rewarding time of the day. Her fun and joy would help deflect the anxiety of the long wait before the next phone call. I would know just after the cub's third feed during this her first full day with Wendy the amount of milk she had accepted and whether there were any other tell-tale signs that might be giving cause for concern.

"Don't worry, Storm's fine," were Wendy's brief but emphatic words.

"Storm did you say, you mean the cub, but when......," my voice died away as Wendy, enthusiastic as always, continued.

"Roger and I decided to give her a name. We thought 'Storm' was appropriate. From what you told us she was lost because of bad weather and it was so rough when she arrived here last night. You never said you'd given her a name either."

"No, I didn't. Storm, sounds good," I interrupted. "But what about her feeding, has she taken enough milk today?"

"No problems at all." Wendy was typically direct. "She's had three feeds already, and taken between three to four ounces each time. She's just had the last and she's now in her box fast asleep. She's passed her first droppings, too, and no problems there it seems. I reckon we may have caught her just in time. Roger's late in tonight, so if you want to speak to him......"

"No, no," I continued, "its great news; and you're obviously okay for Ostermilk. I'll ring again this time tomorrow night, if that's alright with you."

I put the phone down. I sat for a while longer in my study, more relieved than of late and let my mind run over recent events. It was quiet and the room was lit by just the single light over my desk. Pray God, I thought to myself, that our luck holds.

I then joined Helen and Olivia for our supper. Inevitably Helen cooked a good meal, and it was, if possible, always shared together as a family at the end of the working and school day. Nevertheless the contents of the phone call a few minutes previously made this occasion unforgettable for me alongside my dear wife and our lovely daughter. I felt an exhilarating sensation taking over me and it was good to relax. The tension of the last forty-eight hours was easing, and we enjoyed ourselves.

We discussed the choice of name that Roger and Wendy had quite spontaneously given the cub and told Olivia the circumstances which had caused the cub to become lost and how she was then subsequently rescued. I recalled how my very first orphaned otter cub had been rescued by Bob Cooke's springer spaniel and how I had driven all the way to north Norfolk from my home in Bristol in the most dreadful weather to collect her.

"Both were probably victims of a storm, Olivia," interrupted Helen, "or at least from the consequences of previously very bad weather".

So we all agreed that 'Storm' was to be the cub's name; it was appropriate and relevant to her circumstances. But Helen and I knew that the young male barn owl was as much to blame as the bad weather for splitting up Storm's family. Bob's cub too, rescued from the tidal channel, may well have also been the victim of some outside influence. On both occasions there had been prolonged poor weather with low cyclonic pressure, both in the North Sea and the Bristol Channel. I was aware, however, that bitch otters feel the need to move to an alternative holt, to safer ground when their cubs are about six weeks of age. Perhaps it is an unnecessary move and in the process other outside factors can intervene which otherwise would have been avoided.

The name Storm, evocative and emotive, reflected recent events. Now it would become part and parcel of our everyday conversations.

More phone calls over the next forty-eight hours confirmed that Storm was regularly taking good quantities of milk and was sleeping well in between times. Storm was showing her first signs of independent movement between feeds; she was beginning to explore of her own accord, and was responding to Wendy's promptings to play. Was this perhaps an indication that her recovery was now under way?

I was planning to visit the Forest with Helen and Olivia, and at the same time to complete a first gentle photographic session with Storm; indeed Olivia had yet to see her and obviously was very excited. It would mean a very late night for Olivia, who was presently at the local Weare First School. Nevertheless she would have the weekend to recover. Much more to the point, Helen and I had resisted rushing over the River Severn for two reasons. I had been nervous of the cub surviving any length of time, and Helen and I both wanted to share together the joy of Olivia experiencing her first close encounter with a wild otter cub.

We were all very excited as we left Somerset and soon we were crossing the Severn bridge for what was going to be in fact the first of several trips in the coming weeks. Fish and chip supper in Lydney went down well before we were soon being introduced to Derek Martyn, the photographer, who was a long-standing friend of Roger and Wendy.

I gently woke Storm. She had been asleep, stretched out on her towels and soft pullovers in a cardboard Walkers crisps box next to the all-night stove.

"Hello, how are you feeling now," I enquired softly.

"Better, much better. I don't feel half as hungry as I did. I'm really warm and it's very peaceful and quiet here, just as it was in our holt. Wendy's dogs wander in and out of the room from time to time; I sense them sniffing around close to me but she's told me not to be frightened by them."

"You've met Helen briefly before, and Olivia has come this time, too. She really wants to get to know you. Hopefully you will become great friends."

"Who's the other voice?" interrupted Storm.

"That's Derek, I've invited him to take some photographs. You won't mind me holding you, will you, whilst he takes the pictures. At the same time we'll weigh and measure you, that's all very important in helping you to get better. So don't be frightened."

The next half-hour or so passed quietly. Storm was obviously nervous at another new person in her life who pointed a strange object at her, and which then 'clicked' frequently. So she promptly spent a penny into the pocket of my smock! I handled her very carefully, talking to her quietly all the while, and stroking her gently. That brought home to me just how tiny and light she was, so there was no great surprise in the room when her weight on the scales showed as only 1lb 7ozs. Yet I was convinced she had put on some weight since being brought to Wendy! A few final shots were completed with Wendy and Olivia and I decided that was enough for the first session.

I returned Storm to her cardboard holt and put the box by the stove. What was it about cardboard boxes filled with old sweaters and an otter cub placed next to all-night stoves? This was Bob's cottage on the coast road at Salthouse all over again!

"We have to go now. Olivia, like you, is a growing girl and needs her sleep too. But that wasn't too bad was it?" I said quietly to Storm. "I am arranging for Derek to come back and I or rather we will see you again soon. Don't forget, just go on taking your milk and stay warm and you'll find you will really start to improve. Nothing worrying you now?" I enquired.

"No not really, I'm settling in and it's nice."

However Storm seemed unsure, and I waited for a moment. Then as I half expected, she continued.

"I still worry about my Mum you know, and my brothers too. I know they were little horrors but really I was quite fond of them. I think of them all late at night when it's quiet in here, and I hear the wind and the rain outside. We used to roll up together and then in turn Mum would wrap herself around us. Don't get me wrong but I miss that, a comforting feeling of togetherness; I feel I am all alone."

"No, I can understand that completely; there's nothing like a mother's embrace. I have seen it so often with Helen and Olivia. Nor a father's for that matter........"

I didn't try to explain to Storm how in her 'ottery' world a father's affection, in her case the dog's, would never be experienced, and that her mother's chosen mate would probably only encounter his male offspring again to hound them off his chosen territory.

"Do you think they're alright?" Storm continued after a few moments. "I am upset because I know I will never see them again."

I was becoming concerned that any unnecessary worry might jeopardise Storm's recovery.

"I am sure they will survive," I replied in up-beat mood. "Your Mum was pretty tough and was taking all the right decisions for you three. It was just unfortunate that she was spotted by the barn owl, who for some reason best known to himself then attacked her. Your Mum's natural instincts could have never predicted that. I bet they're all snug in their new holt tonight and she will be waiting for the bad weather of the last couple of weeks to clear before remarking her territory. Anyway I will keep in touch with Graham and Francesca and see if there's any news from the area close to where you were found."

"Will you do that for me?" Storm now appeared much more contented but also rather tired.

"Of course," I assured her, "and don't forget when you have overcome this setback, you will be coming to live with our other otters and Helen and Olivia too. So that will be good, won't it. Now you get some sleep and I'll see you again soon."

I hoped I had reassured her. I took a last lingering look at the tiny body. Exhausted, she was quickly asleep in the same position as I had placed her, stretched out over a soft pullover. I noted that I had yet to see her curled up tight in the typical ottery sleeping position; hopefully as she gained strength and matured that would happen naturally but tonight there was no mother, no bitch to draw her into a soft and comforting underbelly.

"Take care, Storm," I whispered.

Over several evenings I continued my regular phone calls checking Storm's progress, and there were no setbacks as Storm steadily improved. Wendy confirmed a routine of four milk feeds a day with up to four ounces of milk being taken at every feed; indeed Wendy was sticking steadily to her plan of 'a little but often', and hopefully therefore a successful outcome with Storm. She was sleeping well between feeds and was also beginning to enjoy 'finger' play with Roger from time to time, responding in the manner of a kitten. Her droppings were of a good texture and colour and Wendy was also encouraging her to pass these regularly both in time and place.

However naggingly in the back of my mind was a warning, originally and firmly impressed upon me in my Norfolk days when I was working as Philip Wayre's pupil with his private and unique collection of animals and birds. For example, whenever we hatched a rare species of duckling or pheasant, or when an orphaned or injured deer fawn or seal pup was brought to his farm he always advised caution when the staff thought the creature was doing well. Three days, three weeks, three months; at those specific times, he reckoned, there could be real hurdles to be overcome. Looking back some did succumb when previously all seemed to be going well, and his warnings thirty years previously were to be uncannily prophetic with Storm. But for the moment all appeared well.

A fortnight later Helen, Olivia and I, and two close friends Steve and Hazel Beckett, were on our way for a second photographic session with Storm. They were to be the first of very many people to acquaint themselves with Storm. The routine of the trip was enjoyably the same, particularly for Olivia, for during the fish and chip supper eaten whilst we sat in our five seater van, she related to Steve and Hazel everything that happened on the previous occasion and which might occur again that evening. It was good for Helen and I to hear Olivia so enthusiastic, marvellous to witness how much detail she had remembered at such an early age. She is still as observant to this day. Soon we were experiencing the warmth of Wendy's welcome again and Derek prepared the lenses for his camera.

"I hear you're going on well," I began as I sat close to Storm.

"Yes I am," replied Storm. "I feel so much stronger; I sleep well at night now. In fact, I often sleep right through until my first feed. Of course when I was in our holt Mum would feed at least twice in the night, first at dusk and then again just before first light. Whilst back for a while in the middle of the night we would always try to grab a feed off her. Inevitably my brothers snatched her attention, and it always seemed to be my turn to suckle just when she was preparing to leave. So I would go to sleep hungry when I could have done with more milk."

"You have a late night feed with Wendy, don't you?" I enquired.

"Roundabout eleven o'clock, before she goes to bed"

"So tell me about your day," I continued.

"In the morning Wendy wakes me; we're all up early here. I have my breakfast, then I'm allowed to wander around for a while. I have some favourite soft toys in a large box whilst Roger and Wendy go to work and I have a second feed at lunchtime with Wendy when she returns. Roger stays with me after I have been fed in the evenings, more rough and tumble play just as I experienced with my brothers but that's fun too." Storm concluded.

"Will you be okay for some more photographs tonight? This time however, a couple of close friends, who have been very supportive of our work with otters, are going to share the experience. I will introduce you to them; Olivia has told them all about you and how you came to be lost and then found."

Storm was very good natured as we passed her between us, and far less nervous than before. She felt noticeably heavier; on the scales she weighed in at 2 lbs 8 ozs, so she was gaining weight at the rate of an ounce per day. Again I kept the session brief and as soon as Hazel had been introduced to, and photographed with Storm, we returned her to her box.

Hazel and Steve had travelled most of the west coast of Scotland and the Isles, hoping to catch a glimpse or even the occasional sign of wild otters. Now to be so close to a wild cub was spontaneously confirmed by both of them as a special moment in their lives together.

For a while we all talked about otters and obviously about Storm's plight in particular. In turn, Steve and Hazel shared their many abortive attempts particularly those when, according to either informed locals or by the law of averages, they should have been successful. They would wait beside the remote beaches of sea lochs, would climb to the still waters of lochans in high summer on Skye or on Mull, and seemingly on just about every other island in the Inner Hebrides. A highlight of their reminiscences was of Steve watching Hazel move off to observe from a good potentially good lochside location whilst he stayed some distance away in the car. A short time later Steve glanced up to see a large dog otter passing very close to the vehicle, trundling unconcernedly to the beach. He thought this was going to be his wife's long awaited moment. However as luck would have it, the otter headed off in completely the opposite direction. Hazel was not amused with that particular story being repeated in company, and I guess rather exaggerated too!

Sadly, our dear friend Steve was to pass away shortly after meeting Storm for the first time. I still remember with pleasure his face wreathed in smiles at having Storm so close to him, which in turn triggerd cherished memories on the pitfalls of 'otter watching'. Since that evening I can recall the countless happy faces of friends, or of casual acquaintances and guests at lectures who have just glimpsed Storm for the first time. I can only begin to imagine the long-term impressions of Storm treasured by those same people.

I left Olivia talking quietly with Storm. She was gently stroking her. I guessed Olivia was setting out their future plans together in the way so typical of excited youngsters. So I moved across the room to thank Derek.

"I never thought I'd be coming back here for a second shoot." His remark startled me and I looked at him questioningly. "Do you know as well as my photography that I keep and breed pigs for a living?" he continued.

"I had no idea," I managed to respond, still unable to see the connection between pigs and Storm.

"From time to time after the sows have farrowed, we can spot a young'un that isn't going to make it. Some would call them 'the runt of the litter'. You always have this gut feeling about them. No matter how much you try and help them they'll give up on you and over the years you're nearly always proven right for sure. Well I didn't want to say anything to you the last time, or to disappoint you, but I never thought that your cub...."

"Storm," I interrupted.

"Yes Storm, that she would ever make it. She looked, well she looked poor, just like one of my piglets."

"So it's a tribute to Roger and Wendy." I said "that...."

"Oh aye, they've pulled her back from the brink alright," Derek continued, "and tonight, well, she doesn't look at all bad, does she."

"Is it safe then to say I'll see you again," I ventured.

"I think so; I certainly hope so, she's a pretty little mite. Give me a ring when you're ready."

I went back to the cardboard box. Storm was asleep, stretched out but still not curled up yet, and Olivia was quietly watching over her. We whispered our good-byes and soon were on our way home. Lydney was quiet although the chip shop was still open for late night customers, its bright lights standing out against the darkened shapes of the other shops in the same rank. As I slowed by the flashing beacons of the pedestrian crossing, I caught the inviting smell of freshly cooked batter on the night air.

Upstream of the Wye bridge, I glimpsed the fast running waters of the river which were, no doubt, swollen by the recent heavy winter rains. I felt a sense of foreboding too as we crossed the Severn bridge and could only imagine the turbulent tidal waters below. Instinctively I felt we were all thinking of wild otters at that moment, except for Olivia who by now had joined her new found friend Storm in an ottery dream. I was reflecting on how wild bitch otters, particularly those with litters of cubs at this time of year, cope with night upon night of wretched weather. I found myself feeling especially concerned for Storm's mother and her boys. Where was she at this moment, and were they all still alive?

The phone call came at a quarter to six. Roger's tone clearly showed his concern.

"Storm's not taken any milk at her evening feed a few minutes ago. Nor did she at lunchtime. I thought I should let you know."

My heart stopped a beat and my mind momentarily froze. Before I could respond, Roger was continuing.

"She doesn't look that bad in herself, bright-eyed and she's quite active, just as she has been of late; you know, playing with me. She was okay early this morning, but she's now turning her nose up at the milk for some reason or another. I was thinking of calling in the vet."

By now I was beginning to think more rationally.

"I'm not keen on a vet at this stage, Roger," I replied, "once we start injections for no obvious reason, we'll be on a hiding to nothing."

"I must admit I tend to agree," added Roger, "particularly since she really appears to be alright in herself. The only other thing I've thought of is perhaps to try her on some solid food, I can get some tonight from the local mini-market. They're open late."

"It's an idea," I said. "Presumably you haven't given her access to water, have you, so that she could have become wet and cold,"....

"No,"....

"And there's been no major change in her surroundings, not been frightened by one of your dogs?" I was thinking of every other possible reason why Storm should go off her food so suddenly .

"No, there's been nothing. She's been going on fine since you were here last. She's become increasingly playful and responsive, coming on a treat in fact. No, leave it with me David, we'll try tinned cat food or something. I'll ring you later."

Helen knew instinctively that the call had been about Storm.

"Trouble," she said without even glancing at me as she prepared the meal.

"What's wrong?" Olivia's voice was immediately anxious too.

"It's Storm," I started.

"Storm's going to be alright, she's not going to die, is she?" Olivia's tone quickly reflected her unease.

"No, nothing like that," I said rather unconvincingly.

Helen recognised my worry. She knew I really wanted to be with Roger and Wendy to make a visual judgement on Storm. After a moment's silence, she added,

"Well, you remember what Philip has told you time and time again whenever you take on a stray........"

"Told me what?" I interrupted sharply.

"Three days, three weeks, and surely you have realised it's just about three weeks since she was found."

"I know, I know. Still they're going to try her on some solid food, and will ring me later on."

My enthusiasm for our forthcoming meal had been instantly lost. Supper that evening became a dull affair which was unfair on Helen and especially on Olivia. But I could not put Storm's so sudden a loss of appetite out of my mind. Later sadly, and regrettably too, Olivia realised that I was rather distant during her bedtime story.

Inevitably the evening passed slowly. I was uncertain whether to ring Roger myself or to wait for what seemed an age for the promised call. Whilst reading or writing fitfully, any conversation between Helen and myself certainly lacked any continuity or conviction.

"That will be Roger now," I heard Helen calling me.

It was nearly ten o'clock, and the suspense had been totally draining.

However, this time, his tone of voice was instantly different.

"Well, you won't believe it," he started, "she's cleared a whole dishfull of catfood, tuna Whiskas to be precise, and just at this moment our Sal's giving her some more; and she's taking it, no trouble," he added.

"Great news," I replied. The relief was enormous. "So she's weaning herself."

"Just like that. I don't think she'll take any more milk now, tho' of course we'll try. But I can see her from here, she's putting it away like a good 'un."

"Can you buy some more tins until I can bring a supply over?" I interrupted. "I wanted to come in a few days time in any case. I was planning to bring her some meat and fish, but I did not want to be too presumptive, ..."

"Like counting your chickens," laughed Roger.

"In case of any setbacks," I continued "and I thought we'd had one tonight. And while I think of it, after the events of this evening, I think we'll have to review our ideas on how old we think she is."

"She's clearly older than she looks. I reckon she's been losing out on her mother's milk for some time and whatever happened recently was the final straw. Do you remember those triplets we reared for you all those years ago? Then the little bitch cub needed all Wendy's attention to pull her through, and yet you had been supplying all the food their mother could need; and literally on a plate in front of her. A female cub can certainly lose out if there is more than one dog cub in the litter. However the Whiskas appears to have done the trick tonight."

"I'll see you in a few days," I concluded, "and well done!"

I excitedly told Helen the news, but wondered whether I should disturb Olivia. Against Helen's advice, I did break her sleep. How much she understood we would know in the morning but I certainly slept better that night than I could have imagined a few hours previously.

Olivia had indeed gathered the good news and went off to school with Helen to tell her classmates all about the virtues of tuna Whiskas for otter cubs. In turn, my first call of the day was to a contemporary from school-days, Robin Crick, who for many years had been a buyer for a firm of wholesale fish merchants trading in the heart of the old city of Bristol. He had come to my aid on countless previous occasions when I was suddenly searching for half a stone of this or that. After a brief resumé of Storm's rescue so far, yes again he could help, and yes he did have available a stone or so of 'as small as possible' sprats which could be dropped mid-morning on the second delivery round in north Somerset .

My plan was to separate a small number, perhaps twenty or so, from the frozen block. I would wrap them individually in cling film, put them in a plastic container, encased and sellotaped in polystyrene, and post them, suitably addressed, to Lydney.

I wanted Storm to have the nourishment from oily fish as soon as possible and similarly to sample her first ox-heart and liver. The latter I planned to take with me on my next journey, but I reckoned it would be possible to have the fish there by the following morning. I sifted through the sprats, selecting the smallest which were really no bigger than large whitebait. The remainder were kept frozen to be used later. Then they would be mixed with other varieties of seasonally fresh fish, and fed to the individual otters in our family group, all of whom had their own particular likes and dislikes.

Finally, I stored the package in one of our freezers. Much later that afternoon, and just before the five thirty deadline, the 'cold' box was popped over the local post office counter to be weighed and stamped first-class before being placed into a waiting mail bag. Unsuspectingly Storm's first fish supper was on its way. However, the meal would not be quite the same for her as if it had been brought to her from the local stream or pond by her wild mother, or indeed tasted and shared alongside her brothers in the remote holt on Exmoor.

'Stormforce' is the dramatic and true tale of one of Britain's rarest and most beautiful mammals, a bitch otter called Storm.

'Stormforce' is the remarkable story of her survival.

The bonding process with Helen....   *....and with Olivia and myself.*

Ostermilk No 2 had been Wendy's successful standby substitute milk for many years; I had used it when rearing orphaned roe deer fawns in the Norfolk collection of the naturalist Philip Wayre over 30 years previously.

A month later; spending time acquainting myself with Storm.

© Derek Martyn

© Derek Martyn

Six months later and Storm was already showing the profile of a young adult otter.

Storm also has a fascination for woolly hats, particularly Sally Mordike's, (née Duncan) from Canberra, Australia.

The impact Storm will have on Olivia's life will surely be ongoing and memorable.

Helen and I on magical Lundy years ago!

Olivia, in the mid-summer of 1999, has other close animal friends.

Sian, a wild but orphaned bitch cub was hand-reared by Mr and Mrs Weir on the Island of Mull. Nick Gordon filmed her close to his island home and before she went south to spend her life at the Otter Trust in Suffolk. This photograph also illustrates the 'waterproof' qualities of an otter's coat. Air trapped between the outer and inner coats acts as insulation. Some of it escapes on the otter's entry into the water and rises to the surface, often leaving a tell-tale trail of bubbles. No doubt this gave rise to Gavin Maxwell's 'Ring of Bright Water'.

This could well have been Storm's wild mother.

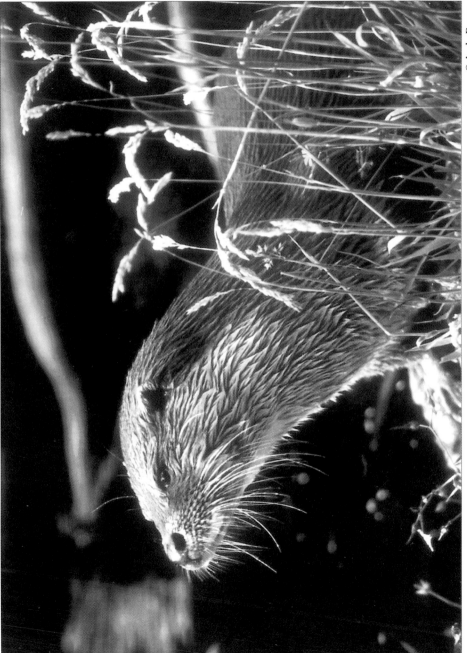

Left: Rowan (pictured) and Houdini reared many cubs throughout the 1980s

Middle: Cider, a gentle giant and bred at the Otter Trust, near Bungay in Suffolk, was a gift from Philip and Jeanne Wayre.

Bottom: Willow was my most prolific breeding bitch. She is pictured here with her first offspring, a half-grown bitch cub.

© Ian Anderson.

Above and Below © Helen Chugg

Cider's son Blackthorn, who was a chip off the old block, was father (by different bitches) to both Ripple and Pebble. At the Tamar Otter Sanctuary, it was difficult to catch Ripple and her triplets together, or at least with all the family looking towards the camera at the same time....

....however, Pebble was more obliging with her twins.

Over the years my otters have contributed to many high quality wildlife series. Here from the early 1980s is Fred during filming for Gerald Durrell's 'The Amateur Naturalist'.

Above:
Sarah Byatt (director)
Warwick Sloss
(cameraman) and
Carwyn Arnold (my
assistant) working
with Storm in the River
Lynher at Bathpool
Bridge for the BBC
NHU's 'Otters, the
Truth'.

Left:
Warwick was now
undoubtedly her friend.

Above: I have never ceased to be amazed by Storm's ability to work in close proximity with strangers. Here, in heavy rain, she is with the presenter John Nettles for West Country Television's 'Animal Passions' at the Tamar Otter Sanctuary.

Below: A successful shoot. John Nettles, Olivia, Storm and myself, still in heavy rain! (P.S. Pebble and her twin cubs were asleep in the 'holt' just behind us.)

Above: Bob Cooke, auxiliary coastguard and man of the North Norfolk marshes in June 1967. His English springer spaniel, Judy, 'fetched' my first otter cub on Boxing Day 1966.

Left: Frank Owen, who encouraged me in the beginning, by the Teifi Pools, near Tregaron, in 1962.

Below: Bob and Joan Cooke's cottage overlooks Salthouse Broad and is where this great adventure began.

Above: Storm in tight close-up is always the requirement. She was filmed by Martin Smith in North Norfolk both in November 1998 for ITV's Survival 'The Wensum Year' and also again in May 1999 for the BBC NHU's 'Living Britain'.

Below: 'Tell them it's our future too!'
    'I will Storm, I promise.'

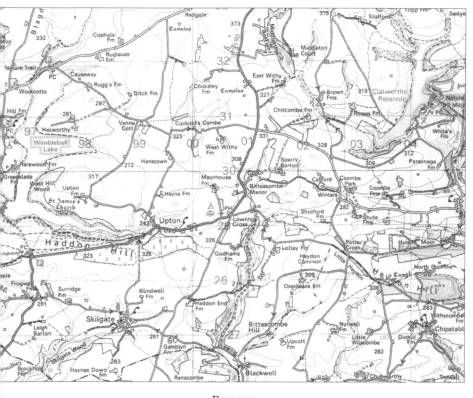

Exmoor

'.....he knew that otters had been spotted in the vicinity, and more often than not close to Clatworthy and Wimbleball reservoirs.'

SIX

"STORM LOVES MY DADDY YOU KNOW"

I made two relevant phone calls amongst many others in the next thirty-six hours. The first was quite deliberately half an hour after the package was posted. I knew that Storm would have finished her third regular feed of the day at about half past five. So there was both the heartening confirmation that Storm had continued well on her new diet of catfood throughout the day, and also the accompanying message to look out for the 'box'.

The second call was again to Wendy before she returned to work the following afternoon. Yes, the sprats had arrived safely and were still frozen. The postman had been none the wiser, and after quickly thawing a couple of fish, then chopping them to mix into the catfood, Storm had promptly cleared the dish. Great news!

So in just forty-eight hours Storm had progressed from a cub 'on the bottle' to a cub now comfortably on solid food. Some transformation which indicated along with her continuing small size that she herself was not exaggerating when she had told me beforehand of constantly missing out on her mother's milk.

Whatever had happened to Storm in those fateful six or seven weeks after her birth was now behind her; in the three to four weeks of bottle feeding she had gained considerable ground, but now a new chapter in her life was about to begin. We had to consolidate her progress on solid food, steadily reducing the diet of cat food, and increasingly replacing it with small quantities of ox-heart, liver and a variety of fish. Roger and Wendy had completed all that I could have asked of them. The time was now rapidly approaching for Storm to be with Helen and myself, and especially to grow into maturity alongside other otters and with her new friend Olivia.

So work had to start in earnest in preparing both an indoor pen and an outdoor enclosure for her; I had not dared to start such work previously for fear of taking her recovery for granted.

As I left Storm with Roger and Wendy for her last spell with them, I did so with considerably more optimism and I felt that finally she was on the road to recovery.

"Olivia, can I ask you a favour?"

"Do you have to right now?," came a rather distant reply from the far side of the rocky outcrop where I was sitting with Helen.

"You'll do it for daddy, won't you?" added Helen, but rather less enthusiastically than I had hoped.

"Do what, for goodness sake?" Olivia's voice was suddenly much louder as she appeared high above me with a rather exasperated expression on her face. Moments later Sasha our English springer spaniel rushed into view. Her tail wagging furiously, she had just retrieved her stick for the umpteenth time that afternoon, and had promptly dropped it with unerring accuracy right into my lap. Her eyes fixed on me and with one foreleg raised, she waited expectantly for the slightest movement from me which might indicate my next throw. With my back wedged into a natural slit in the granite rock, I was looking south-west towards Pendeen Watch from the coastal cliff path just beyond Gurnard's Head.

"Are you listening to me?" I asked.

"Yes, I'm hearing you. Just tell me what you want," replied Olivia rather impatiently.

"Well, I've been thinking about *Stormforce*, and...."

"Your father has been sat here gazing out to sea, and hasn't been listening to a word I've been saying all afternoon." Helen had now intervened again.

"Am I going to be allowed to ask Olivia or not?" I was beginning to wish I had not bothered.

"Go on then, you poor old soul." Helen then flinched as I waved my arm roughly in her direction and a still panting, but ever eager, Sasha shot between us thinking her stick had again been thrown into the nearby bracken. Simultaneously cans of fizzy drinks, bananas and apples vanished in a flurry of fur and legs.

"Sssh Mummy, let Daddy tell us, and you listen as well," Olivia was adamant at last.

I explained to Olivia that I had now reached a critical stage in the completion of the manuscript for *Stormforce*. I had written most of the text, and it was now being typed, checked, and then retyped. However, there were still important parts of Storm's life-story to be recalled.

"Olivia, you realise that I have regularly been with Storm late at night reminiscing about her brief life with her mother, and how she came to be rescued."

"You have always spent hours with her, haven't you, particularly when she first came to live with us? Sometimes after you had seen me to bed, I would peep out of my bedroom window and I could see a red glow coming from a window in the roof by the garage." Olivia could always remember detail so accurately. "You were with her then, weren't you?"

"That was when we were in Somerset, and the window was a roof light that allows daylight to enter a building when it is otherwise enclosed. You're talking about Storm's indoor pen, and the red glow came from the infra-red lamp which I would turn on at night. That gave her extra warmth which was vital when she was young. Obviously she didn't have her mother's own body heat to protect her." I paused and then added smiling, "and there was I thinking you were fast asleep."

"No wonder she's so fond of you; and it's because of the book you are frequently with her at night now, aren't you?"

"You will still see a light on late, but not a red glow these days. She is now a mature lady and rarely needs any extra warmth. In fact, British otters don't need heat as such, even when the cubs are born in the depths of winter. You remember Blackthorn, don't you? I can recall quite vividly coming home to Somerset from the Otter Trust with Blackthorn's father Cider; Cider was also, as you know, to become one of Storm's closest friends. It was early November time, and I ran Cider with the bitch Rosie from that very first night of his arrival. His single male cub Blackthorn was born early in the following January, indicating that he had successfully mated with her during the next forty-eight hours. There were continuous hard frosts at night throughout the first three weeks of Blackthorn's life. It was that cold I had the devil's own job breaking the ice just to provide his mother with drinking water. His birth had taken me by surprise, so it was far too late to contemplate installing any extra heat; but mother and son survived as I packed in ever more quantities of dry bedding to combat the cold. Anyway, let's get back to Storm," I concluded.

"I've often seen Storm drying herself on her towels. When she's wet and cold, she really throws herself into it."

"Yes, that proves how vital reedbeds are for otters on their

117

territories; they often use the dense vegetation of sedges or rushes as a daytime couch, where they can rest and stimulate their coats by constant grooming and rubbing."

"Okay, but you still haven't told me yet where I can help." Olivia was becoming restless.

"I'm putting Storm's account together, often with her help of course, but there's one particular chapter...."

"That wouldn't be the one, would it, about the various television programmes and lectures we have done together with Storm?" Olivia had cleverly worked out just where I needed her help.

"That's right. Storm's not the best at concentrating, particularly at night, when naturally she's very active. I manage to put down a few notes on which to build a storyline later, but in no time she wants me to play with her especially when she's swimming in her tank. Then of course it's towel time as you've mentioned, ending with her finally rubbing herself dry, either in my lap or against my smock. It's a battle just to keep her talking. Then suddenly she's tired, so she promptly stops and goes to sleep. Rather like somebody else I know!"

Olivia smiled. After a pause she added, "Do you want me to help you with the details for that chapter?"

"If possible please, and as I indicated a while back, that way you will be contributing greatly to the book."

"I'd love to," responded Olivia excitedly. "I could look out my autograph book and my scrapbook. They'll have all the information and photographs I have kept."

"That would be ideal. Thanks. We'll start tonight, shall we? I have already chosen the first story I want to use."

Olivia went back to gently teasing Sasha in and out of the outcrops of rock on the headland, attempting to confuse her by always hiding her stick somewhere different. Sasha was in her element, furiously seeking and inevitably, it seemed, always succeeding in fetching it from amongst the long coarse grasses. Helen and I could sit for long periods of time enjoying Olivia and Sasha, whilst simultaneously gazing towards the lighthouse at Pendeen and the western Atlantic beyond. Today with the exceptional light and even without using the field glasses, I could make out the shapes on the horizon that are the islands of the Scillies. Occasionally I spotted a procession of gannets tracking deliberately towards the same islands, and though at a distance, they were so conspicuously sparkling white against a turquoise sea. In file or irregular V, alternately gliding and flying in perfect rhythm, and without checking to dive or circle for fish, they pushed on past the occasional coasters which, given the fair weather, had cut inside the Longships lighthouse off Lands End. Closer to hand, the highlights we were awaiting would be either the occasional glimpses of the local cock stonechat, which resplendent on golden yellow gorse, could, because of our presence, appear to re-establish his territory. We might also recognise the strident calls of the peregrines above the roar of the Atlantic breakers from a dark gully below us. Would the falcon again pursue, as we had previously observed, her aerial but territorial game of cat and mouse over the cliffs with one of the resident buzzards? Sadly today, nothing transpired. So in the absolute beauty of the place, I continued to gaze seawards and pondered about '*Stormforce*'.

"Shall I tell you about one of the very first occasions I worked with Storm and then you will understand the details we need to illustrate for the reader? By the way, both you and Mummy were present."

"Yes please, it will give me an idea of how a story develops." Olivia was sitting on her bed, excited and eager to contribute to her important role in the completion of '*Stormforce*'.

"It began with Dora Westlake, who is the daughter of close friends of ours. She had won a regional round in the *Daily Telegraph's* 'Young Naturalist of the Year' competition. For that she had written an essay about otters and their problems, and had previously photographed Storm to illustrate her project. The prize was to be presented to her in the Visitor Centre at Hinkley Point Nuclear Power Station. The parent company, Nuclear Electric, was one of several national companies that had sponsored the competition."

"Hinkley rings a bell," interrupted Olivia, "you've brought me souvenirs from the gift shop there."

"Yes, I've been there with Storm on several occasions now and....."

"You've told me another story about Hinkley and otters. Wasn't it something to do with Storm's mother?"

"I explained that her mother could well have made her way onto Exmoor via the headwaters of a stream that ultimately spills out into the Bristol Channel very close to the nuclear station.

However I have already recorded that remarkable fact in another chapter. In the meantime, let's go back to Dora's presentation. Everything was prepared meticulously well, a tank in which she would be able to swim, straw bales on which to climb and towels on which to dry herself....."

"..... and her sprainting mat to make her feel at home" interrupted Olivia enthusiastically, "so really everything was just the same as we do today."

"That's right, and as you know, the moment she gets tired and has finished drying herself, that's when she will look to climb into my arms......."

"......For a huggle!" Olivia blurted out her favourite word remembering when she too needs comfort and reassurance. To 'huggle' is for Olivia and myself the cross between a cuddle and a hug, and it's during huggles when photographers can get very good close-up photos both of Storm and Olivia!"

"After the prize had been presented, we concluded with a successful press photocall with both Dora and Storm, and the pattern for future lectures had been set. You see, I had already taken Storm out in her travelling crate several times previously in order to accustom her to the movement of the van and strange noises. Those dummy runs had always been at different times of the day so she could become accustomed to being woken up and to travelling outside her normal daily routine."

"Is all this leading into another occasion?"

"Yes, it is. Jacqui Lucas who was then, and still is now, Information Officer at Hinkley had masterminded the original preparations. Through her subsequent recommendation, I then received an invitation to present Storm at Nuclear Electric's Headquarters at Barnwood in Gloucestershire, to celebrate John Collier Cup Day." This is the annual summer occasion when the staff of the various companies and power stations enjoy a competitive but friendly open sports day. I was to offer an alternative option for their guests by giving talks in one of their lecture theatres on the problems that wild otters face.

"You're talking about the time we took Grandma and Grandpa. I stayed for the first lecture, went around all the sideshows and then came back late in the afternoon for the last performance."

"Aaaah, but you only know half the story," I exclaimed, and now Olivia was really intrigued.

"The night before, when as usual I had been sat quietly for

some while with Storm, she suddenly attacked me without any warning. She was chittering loudly, and her voice growled into a crescendo. There was absolutely nothing I could do to calm her."

"Did you have any idea what it was all about?," enquired Olivia nervously.

"None whatsoever. I decided to try and sit it out for a while, but in the ensuing scrum she ripped the watch off my wrist and at the same time nipped me quite nastily both on my forearms and thighs. As she continued to charge between the straw bales that made up her sleeping den, I decided to leave immediately and to come back for my watch later."

"And did you find it?" Olivia continued anxiously.

"It was near midnight when I eventually returned. But even from the light of the infra-red lamp I could see that Storm was still very disturbed. She immediately started chittering and growling again. Of the watch there was no sign, so I decided it was best to let her settle, for early that next morning, the Saturday, I was due to take her to Barnwood, near Gloucester, for those four lectures."

"So what happened?" Olivia's expression, with her blue eyes wide open, confirmed her natural anxiety.

"I decided to crate and load Storm very early. If everything went wrong, then at least I would have enough time to try a different approach. But exactly what and how I hadn't decided. I was determined to be confident, so as to in no way give her the idea that I might be apprehensive myself. I approached her indoor enclosure gently rattling the bolts as normally in order to awaken her, and to give her time to come to her senses before I was actually in with her."

"And what did she do? Did she go for you?" Olivia's voice was breathless with anticipation.

"Absolutely nothing," I replied;, "she didn't react nastily at all."

"You mean she was just as she had always been?"

"No, she was definitely still wary, and rather tense, but there was none of her out and out aggression. Anyway, I carried her to the travelling crate on the van without any problem and came indoors for breakfast. Everything else I needed had been loaded the night before, and when I reappeared with Helen and yourself to start the journey, Storm appeared quiet and content. You certainly didn't realise that anything was wrong."

"She seemed okay when I left you at the end of the first lecture too."

"Obviously I had been apprehensive when I introduced her.

Nuclear Electric had prepared everything I had asked for in the way of facilities. Maybe Storm was slightly tense, but that first talk went off very well. She went all through her routines, going to the sprainting mat, exploring the four corners of the presentation pen in front of the visitors, and consistently coming back to the tank to swim."

"Then I bet it was back onto her straw bales to roll," added Olivia.

"You would never have guessed her tantrums of the night before, and the plan, as you know, was to complete four presentations during the day. There was an audience of at least two hundred and fifty people on each occasion, and Storm was well behaved considering there were many highly excited youngsters crowding in close."

"When I came back with Grandma and Grandpa, you and mummy looked pretty exhausted, and Storm was nowhere to be seen. Presumably she was asleep in her crate."

"That's right. I had one more presentation to give and I had heard over the public address system that everybody who hadn't already seen Storm, a live British otter, was being encouraged to make their way to the lecture theatre for one final showing. Susan Merrill and Susan Hampton, who together organised our day superbly, popped in to say that the chairman of the company and his wife were heading our way for the finale! However there was just one problem."

"What was that," interrupted Olivia all agog, "go on tell me."

"Well, you were there," I suggested, at the same time glancing secretly at her expression. I paused and waited for another clue from Olivia. Nothing was forthcoming so I continued. "Although Storm had been very good, in fact unbelievably good when being handled, she had in fact chittered quite angrily again when I had put her into her crate at the end of the third talk. That was the first time I had heard the sound since late the previous night. I didn't know whether she had seen and heard enough of people and excited youngsters for that day, or if she would take yet another presentation in her stride after a further break of over an hour."

"I think I now know exactly what you're going to put in this chapter," Olivia said with a mischievous smile.

"I bet you do," I responded immediately. There was no reply from Olivia but I could sense her intense gaze. I knew eventually, and sooner rather than later, that Olivia would admit to what happened next, so I hastened on.

"Sure enough the room became quickly packed, but this time the youngsters were pushing even further forward because of the sheer volume of people crowding in. So the front rows were now almost right beneath me. The VIPs had already come and, if you remember, I covered myself for any last minute histrionics from Storm by saying, and quite truthfully I may add, that handling Storm might prove somewhat difficult. After all I added, it had been a long day for her, especially with the anxiety of travelling. Those first few minutes, along with the introduction to the talk, always passed very rapidly, and in no time I was approaching the open door of her travelling crate into which Storm had sensibly stayed for a rest after lecture three. But at the very moment I turned to the audience to make my final request for them to remain still and quiet, which was a remark that was really aimed at the animated youngsters, I heard Storm chitter in annoyance. My heart dropped. However, there was no alternative but to smile bravely and press on. I put both hands into the crate......"

".......and she bit you!" interrupted Olivia excitedly. "I knew she did, because from where I was sitting with Mummy I could see the expression on your face."

"As I brought her out to face the audience I slid her across my body and kept my right hand, which I knew was almost certain to be bleeding, tucked away in the right hand pocket of my smock. I used my forearm to support her back end and rudder."

"Was your hand paining much?" Olivia was concerned at my demise. She is always very caring but at the same time has difficulty in suppressing her giggles. She invariably finds it funny when I suffer a mishap; but for that matter so does Helen!

"Storm has extremely sharp teeth; they cut you like a razor. It's more a feeling of soreness rather than of pain, especially if she catches you close to a nail or on the softer skin between the fingers. Anyway," I went on, "no one had realised exactly what had happened. So having moved as close as I dared to the youngsters in the front row, I proceeded with my talk."

The grin on Olivia's face was widening.

"Then suddenly, for no immediately apparent reason, all the eyes of the audience looked to their left, my right, instead of directly and intently on Storm, as previously. I couldn't understand it."

"And it was all because of me," Olivia could not contain herself any longer.

123

"Well yes, I suddenly realised. My eyes followed the audience's and there you were, bless your little cotton socks, coming across the enclosure with a couple of Mummy's large white Kleenex tissues. With your hand and the tissues outstretched towards me, I had no alternative but to extend my right hand to allow nurse 'Chaffe' to administer first aid. My cover had been well and truly blown."

"I thought you were pleased I cared," Olivia sounded disconsolate.

"Don't be silly, of course I was. I was very touched and so too were the people watching. Nevertheless my hand looked far worse than it actually was; my skin was wet and sweating, and so the blood appeared to be running across my hand. Still you soon had me tidied up, and I was much more relaxed once the tension had been taken out of the situation. Although it was now the fourth occasion, I remembered completing the presentation in good form stressing many important details for otters generally. It was a successful conclusion to a rewarding day both for the many visitors, there must have been well over a thousand, and for Storm herself."

I looked at Olivia. She was fading fast, having at some time climbed into bed without my realising. Eyes closed, she appeared to be still smiling, her lovely face softly lit by the bedside lamp. There was a long pause.

"So why did she bite you the previous night?" she suddenly asked.

"The reason became apparent a few weeks later. Obviously the date of the Barnwood weekend remained clear in my mind, so I kept a special watch on her behaviour just over six weeks later."

"This is becoming more curious by the minute," insisted Olivia.

"Well, you're quite old enough now to understand that a female animal has to come on heat, or into oestrus to use the technical term, before she can successfully mate or sire with the male in order to become pregnant and have babies."

"I know, it's dog, bitch and cubs with otters, isn't it?"

"That's right; so sure enough almost forty-five days later to the day Storm was very much out of sorts. But this time she was more, well moody would be a better way of describing her; there was far less aggression. It was clear that she had come on heat for the very first time just before the Barnwood lecture; she had become a young adult otter capable of breeding. Obviously it was a very traumatic experience for her, and she didn't want anybody or anything interfering with her."

"Quite right too," came Olivia's immediate comment.

"She's been the same ever since and now the critical hours over the particular days pass by without so much stress. I have learnt now that when I am with her during that period of time, to be around but not around, if you see what I mean. British otters are regularly on heat at an interval of every forty-five days or so, most usually have a sixty-three day pregnancy, and therefore can, and do, breed in every month of the year. Most commonly twins are born, although never more than quads with each cub weighing about 78 grammes at birth."

"So tell me again, when was Storm born?" Olivia was really intrigued now.

"We can only guess. However, it's likely that her mother gave birth between Christmas Day and New Year's Day, that's assuming we were right in reckoning Storm to be about six weeks old when she was discovered.

"So her wild mother mated.... no, let me work it out," Olivia was insistent as I made to continue.

"Sixty-three days, you say. So it must have been about the end of October."

"And that's a very good point to end our first story together," I added. "It makes sense to introduce the facts about bitch otters maturing within the context of Storm's first big public occasion. It's also important to keep to themes, so I thought the next episode we might relate could be of Storm and yourself at the BBC's Pebble Mill studios in Birmingham for 'Wildbunch'. Do you agree?"

This time there was no reply. So I pulled the duvet cover over Olivia, kissed her gently on her forehead and whispered 'night night' quietly into one ear. Still no response. Sometimes, some nights, she will repeat the two words from her semi-consciousness, but now tonight she was already in her dreams, and lost to me. I sat close to her for a little while and wondered just how many other eleven year olds had spent the equivalent of their bedtime story tonight reminiscing about the private and personal life of a wild otter with whom she was also growing up. Did she know just how lucky she was? Indeed, did I realise how privileged I was to be sharing both of their extraordinary lives?"

Olivia had finished at Truro High Preparatory School, Helen was shopping for the weekend groceries in Tesco's, and a little later, we were going to watch the stage version of Wallace and Gromit in the recently refurbished Hall for Cornwall. But instead of joining the dozens of other cars in their monotonous ranks in the supermarket's car-park, Olivia and I had travelled the further mile or so down the estuary towards Malpas. Here we could exercise Sasha close to the local football and cricket pitches, sit on my favourite bench and look across the adjacent mudflats towards Old Kea, where the fields of Trethowell Farm ran gently to the tree-lined waters edge. Luckily the tide was recently on the turn, so there was the likelihood of seeing some interesting waders on the newly exposed mud. I had already realised that Olivia and I would have the time to recall another memorable occasion when she and I worked together with Storm.

Meanwhile some of the birds I particularly wanted her to see were much in evidence. I had enjoyed the resident flock of seventeen black-tailed godwits all winter, and here they were again at unbelievably close range. They were for ever busily probing the mud. Whenever they flighted, with long legs trailing the short distance across the water to the other tidal edge, their bold white rump and wing stripes with broad black tail-bands were very distinctive.

I wanted Olivia to appreciate how waders have evolved varying bill lengths to allow them to reach their food sources at different levels in the mud. It was amazing then, that at this precise moment in time there were four species in front of us to illustrate my theme. Redshank, black-tailed godwit, oyster-catcher and curlew, in ever increasing size, were already on the exposed flats. For Olivia, today, appreciating the range of beaks which allows all waders to share the same feeding grounds without competing for the same food would be enough. But secretly I hoped that maybe in future years, her interest would have grown enough for her to want to learn that the long curved beaks of the curlews were probably probing for some peppery furrow shells, the godwits were enjoying small ragworms, the oyster catchers would have been splitting macomas, whilst the redshanks, ever the sentinels of the tide's edge, would have been satisfied with a meal of mafon worms.

"Do you know Olivia," I began, "I have never ceased to be amazed at how quickly Storm learnt the meaning of certain noises....."

"What were you thinking of in particular?" replied Olivia.

"It didn't take her very long to recognise differences in sounds. For instance the varying 'clunk' of particular car doors being opened and shut, and the subsequent crunch of footsteps on the gravel close to the barn. At first that was very noticeable when we were living in Somerset, because her overnight pen was close to the house.

"I thought she would only know our vehicles, especially the sliding doors on your van," observed Olivia rather astutely.

"Oh no, she would also become very excited when she knew there were extra people or strange vehicles about. I can remember being with her on many occasions when I don't know how or what exactly would alert her, but she would instantly leave what she was doing to listen more intently. Then inevitably, she would make her way to her sprainting mat."....

"And marked her territory."

"Redefined it might be a better way of describing her action. So it was her way, the otter's way, of boosting her confidence for the encounter with the stranger that was surely going to follow. But this particular afternoon I'm not so sure whether it was Storm, or our visitor, who was more excited."

"Who was that then?" asked Olivia intrigued.

"You should remember the lady in question well. It was Michelle Thompson who had come to research Storm for an episode of the BBC children's wildlife programme, 'Wildbunch', and which was being presented at the time from the BBC's Pebble Mill Studios in Birmingham."

"That was a brilliant day in the studios, and I know just why you're going to tell this story too. I was at school when she arrived at our home. But I came home to meet her briefly, and then we took her back to the station......"

".....where, as she alighted from Paddington earlier in the day, I had identified myself by holding up the then current monthly edition of BBC *Wildlife* magazine. I remember when I went to see Storm before introducing her to Michelle, that she was already bouncing around with excitement. You see, again she had deduced that extra and strange footsteps had passed close by. At such moments, as if in anticipation of meeting somebody new, she has a quirky behaviour pattern of somersaulting and simultaneously trying to catch her own tail. Sometimes too she will also lie on her back, then will stretch both upwards and forwards to gently chew the pads of her back feet which she has turned towards her. She'll become quite preoccupied for several minutes."

"You obviously brought her out to meet Michelle in the back garden?"

"Yes, and Storm went through all her regular routines as soon as I released her. I had avoided giving her any idea that day was going to be any different from the countless others when I had taken her out to play. Michelle and I sat together on two of the three all-weather chairs that you know were always strategically placed in exactly the same place for whoever called. I also used to regularly sit on one most nights, and if not being interrupted either by Storm, or poor weather, would reply to my personal correspondence".

"I can remember her always jumping up, either onto the next seat, or directly into your lap. She would be excited, mischievous too, and thoroughly wet after playing in her tank......"

"......or tired having chased you backwards and forwards on your swing," I interrupted.

"....then she would shake herself dry and spray your paperwork. You would tick her off, but nicely though."

"Eventually she would rub herself dry, wriggling from side to side, having slumped into my lap on her favourite towel. Of course, she would also be waiting for her evening meal"

"So it was no different with Michelle"?

"None whatsoever. Michelle was immediatley captivated by Storm. Storm came bouncing towards her at first, her back slightly arched, which is so typical of all the large weasels and always done to put the visitor on his or her back foot. Actually it's never more than a bluff. Then it was her sprainting routine, making sure she was dominant in the garden area, the very same behaviour pattern as her mother and brothers would have been following on their respective territories on Exmoor".

"So she was stating that the garden was hers, wasn't she. I am Storm, I am a young bitch otter and this is my home. You may enter, but first and foremost this is my territory." Olivia had summed it up admirably.

"Storm's behaviour patterns that followed were all that you and I know so well, snatching brief looks and hurried sniffs whilst all the time continuing to check out her enclosure's boundaries. Eventually she climbed on the bales of straw that lay alongside her tank, dipping her head in and out of the fresh water continuously but, as always, so very tentatively at first."

"I bet she kept glancing over to see if you were watching?" Olivia knew Storm very well.

"Yes she did, but finally she submerged slipping in ever so silently as she would have done on her territory in the wild when not wanting to be seen. Only then did she start to roll joyously on her back".

"Did you persuade Michelle to submerge her arm in the tank? That's a fantastic sensation, feeling the body of a wet otter sliding over your skin," remembered Olivia affectionately.

"At first I waited for Storm to use up some of her energy, especially since she was particularly boisterous that afternoon. She seemed to know she needed to impress. Michelle rolled up her sweater, and with a bare arm and a clenched hand immersed them in the cold water. Storm swam tantalizingly ever closer to her, and finally nudged her in friendship".

"Did you warn her she could nip like a playful puppy?" interrupted Olivia excitedly.

"Olivia, you mustn't forget that Storm tests out a visitor's courage, and it was no different with Michelle. However, I must say it was difficult to tell whether it was Storm or Michelle who was becoming more quickly carried away!"

"If you wait long enough Storm eventually always comes out to see you". Olivia had watched Storm's predictable behaviour with total strangers many times.

"Yes she emerged close to Michelle alright, and began to introduce herself, but at the same time".....

".....soaking her, I bet," laughed Olivia.

"Storm shook herself virtually dry in one movement, with all the excess water flying from her outer coat in every direction in one lovely ottery shimmer. Michelle didn't mind; in fact, I have never known anybody to become upset. Then Storm started her slow but methodical process of coming ever closer to the chairs. She's uninhibited by the closeness of a stranger when in her tank, but when that same person is seated, Storm takes her time".

"When I was with you some evenings she used to look for slugs, especially if it had been raining; in fact she became very fond of them," added Olivia. "She'd gobble them up".

"I well remember her excited chittering warning us off, reminding us that the slimy soft creatures were her discovery, and woe betide either of us if we made any attempt to take them off her. Still thankfully there were no live distractions that afternoon, and all the while Michelle had been either on the edge

129

of her seat, or tankside on the straw bales. There had been the widest of affectionate smiles from the first moment she had encountered Storm, and finally when she witnessed Storm in my arms, her expression again summed up everything she felt. Even Mummy popping out into the garden to tell us she was on her way to collect....."

I got no further for suddenly Olivia was pushing me backwards at arms length and Sasha was trying to separate us.

"What about Mummy now," she exclaimed, "she'll be beside herself at Tesco's. Do you realise what the time is?"

Simultaneously as we made to hurry to the car, a very large flock of two or three hundred dunlin swarmed into the creek below us; most were still revealing their off-white underbellies of winter plumage.

"Look, five species of waders now, and one of the smallest, to tell you about...." I began.

"Not now Daddy," I heard Olivia call. Already she and Sasha were well ahead of me.

"I'll tell you about dunlin another time then," I called, as I vainly attempted to catch them both.

"I liked the characters of Shaun the sheep and Gromit best of all. Gromit because of his sense of humour and his costume, the way, although portraying a dog, he walked upright and instead of talking because we know dogs can't talk, he communicated with the others by making all those facial expressions. But I couldn't always keep up with Wallace; he used phrases I didn't understand."

"They were colloquial Lancashire expressions," I explained. "A 'bit steep' for instance, means expensive, 'and there goes my knotty pine', is 'too late it's broken.' Why Shaun?" I enquired, as I continued to enjoy Olivia's vivid descriptions.

"......Shaun, because he moved brilliantly on all fours if you see what I mean, and everytime he stopped he went 'baaa'.... the actor who played his part must have been exhausted by the end of the play." Olivia smiled, and lay back on her pillows, "It was great wasn't it, a good start to the holidays" she murmured. "I enjoyed talking about 'Wildbunch' too, and Mummy wasn't that annoyed with you for being late, yet again. When will you be writing that part up?"

"Soon, tomorrow perhaps. But since at the moment you still seem to be wide awake, I thought we could finish Michelle's and Storm's story".

"So can I tell you what I remember about taking Storm to Pebble Mill?" asked Olivia immediately, "I really liked it there."

"Certainly you can, and in any order you like; I'll just make notes now and will construct a storyline later."

"Where shall I start, there's so much detail. I don't remember much about the journey except it was long, and we took even more time manoeuvering the van in as close as possible to the studio.... and the studio, well that was pitch dark when we first went in, just red and green lights everywhere and an intense bright light and film cameras around two people....."

"They were the programme's presenters," I interrupted.

"......one was a veterinary surgeon.... that was Mark, and the girl was called Janice. Later they gave me their autographs for my collection, they were really nice to me......"

"I remember them being very patient with the other children who were taking part, and also with their parents." I added.

"The children didn't do very well with filling in the squares on the flashing screen. Do you remember Dad, when one of them pressed a button a light stopped flashing and revealed part of an otter." Olivia giggled, "except they didn't know it was going to be

131

an otter.   Then they had to try and guess what animal was eventually going to complete the picture on the screen because it was to be the main attraction on the programme.   Obviously it was Storm, but they had no idea at all did they, and nearly all the lights were out before they guessed correctly....."

"Well.... you very rarely see a British otter in a television studio."

"Then there was that beautiful snowy owl, wasn't there? Let me get this right. The male snowy owl is smaller, and nearly all white, and the female is larger and covered in black flecks. You said it helped her become camouflaged amongst the rocks, particularly when she is lying flat on her nest in mid-summer. And also, before they strike at lemmings for their food, they can appear to be lost against the background of partly melted snow and rocks....."

I knew Olivia had been awestruck by that female snowy, and many times previously I had enthused with her about snowies, which are also one of my favourite birds. I have always felt it vital to pass on to Olivia from an early age the countless wonders of the world natural, at least the few of which I am aware. Peter Scott had been my schoolboy hero; his father Captain Scott, as he lay dying in the tent alongside his already frozen companions at the end of the ill-fated Polar journey, had written to those who would care for his son:

'make the boy interested in natural history; it's better than games
— they teach it at some schools.'

Wild nature still has countless mysteries to be unravelled, even though nearly a century after Captain Scott's wish so much has been discovered.

Indeed, I had already related to Olivia how the female snowy is up to one third heavier than her partner and I was pleased she had already recalled that fact. At first, she did not believe that the females have a sixth sense just prior to the breeding season; that they seem to know if the lemmings, their principle source of food, have not survived the winter well underground and will therefore be scarce. Subsequently, they will perhaps lay only two or three eggs, or even maybe none at all. However in potentially plentiful times up to nine eggs will be laid. Obviously food is hard to find during the harsh winter months, but another amazing fact for Olivia was that the snowy owl is capable of fasting for up to forty days at a time, relying heavily on the thick deposits of fat laid down earlier under its skin. The chances of their survival are also improved by the fact their feathers contain insulating air pockets. They save their energy by moving as little as possible during the long arctic winter on the frozen barren tundra beyond the treeline. Truly remarkable birds indeed.

"Then it was our turn!" exclaimed Olivia animatedly, "Michelle had created a lovely enclosure, hadn't she, with a pool, rocks and grass. Storm looked absolutely great when you released her and they had already put my fluffy otter into several different positions to show you where they wanted to film Storm in close up. But they had forgotten Storm would take her time exploring, and although you had marked the particular spots with her spraint to give the cameras a chance to focus on her, the problem was they were running out of time, weren't they?"

"Olivia, wherever Storm is being displayed I always have a difficulty, as you well know, in persuading everybody who is involved that she needs time to settle, time for her to work through the routines which give her the vital information about her immediate whereabouts, and thus the confidence to behave naturally."

"They were calling for you to encourage Storm into the pool; I seemed to remember you stressing that the moment you stepped inside the enclosure Storm would follow you. In fact, away from where they eventually wanted her to swim....."

"But they insisted, didn't they? And then when Storm immediately ran towards me...."

"The audience went 'aaaaaah' in affection," declared Olivia. "I heard the person in charge...."

"the floor director....."

".....immediately say 'shhhhhhh'."

"Well they were recording sequences of Storm behaving quite naturally, so they could edit them later into the discussion about otters and about Storm in particular...."

".....and then I put my foot in it, didn't I?"

"you mean both feet....."

"......well I forgot that it was live, well you *do* don't you?"

"There I was," I continued, "having just come out of the pen, with the enclosure so brightly lit that there was no way I could distinguish any of the parents and their youngsters in the pitch darkness. I certainly had no idea where you and Mummy were until, no let me finish...." At this point I found myself pushing a highly embarassed but smiling Olivia away from me, ".....until seconds later I heard this instantly recognisable voice say, *'but Storm loves my Daddy you know'!* "Whereupon there was another spontaneous but even louder 'aaaah'..... and yet another lady, and again it wasn't Michelle called out 'cut'. All the lights promptly came up, and there was Mummy trying desperately to dig a hole and disappear." I laughed loudly....

"Sshhhhhhh! Keep your voice down," Olivia promptly scolded me, "or Mummy will hear us. Then she'll find out what you are going to write, and you know she won't approve."

"Sshhhhhh yourself then," I grinned as I crept quietly away, "I'll see you in the morning. God bless you."

"How long ago?" Olivia interrupted.

"Long before Storm was around. I was with one of my first otters, but this time it was something I said which caused another television programme to be stopped. The film recording the story of the book, 'Ring of Bright Water', which was written by the late Gavin Maxwell when he lived at Camusfearna near Glenelg, on the west coast of Scotland with his otters, Mij and Edal....."

"....they weren't British though, were they?" Olivia interrupted yet again.

Olivia smiled, and I stopped slightly frustrated. Most of my time spent piecing the story 'Stormforce' together with Storm had been late at night. Now that Olivia was closely involved, we also reminisced together around her bedtime, or whilst exercising Sasha, or even bird-watching together. Tonight, Olivia was still wide awake. Her smile was followed by a questioning stare, which was accompanied by yet another smile. After a few moments I continued.

"The film was to be premiered at the Odeon cinema, Leicester Square. But Gavin Maxwell was a sick man; he phoned requesting me to cover the publicity by taking one of my otters to London. The late Bill Travers and his wife Virginia McKenna were, along with the otters, the stars of the film, Travers playing the part of Gavin Maxwell, and Virginia McKenna Maxwell's friend and companion. At the BBC's Shepherds Bush Green studios, the Travers' were going to be questioned about the making of the film, and I was to talk about the problems already facing otters in the wild at that time. The pre-recorded programme, called 'Late Night Line Up', was transmitted on BBC2 late on weekday nights."

"I've heard of Virginia McKenna, haven't I?" enquired Olivia.

"She was the founder of the 'Born Free Foundation'. Isn't she responsible for putting animals like lions and dolphins back into the wild; you've given me several newspaper cuttings on her work from the *Daily Mail* for my scrapbook."

"That's right. 'Born Free' was the name of a film she originally made with her husband in East Africa in 1966; it told of lions and their cubs that were befriended by George and Joy Adamson. The story is another 'must' for you to read one day soon. Meanwhile I had travelled to London with my first female otter, Tiki, and soon had her settled close to the recording studio in her travelling crate, and I waited to be told what to do."

"Why did you call her Tiki? The name doesn't sound English at all and it's very different from the names you use now."

"Her male mate was Kon, and I named them both after Thor Heyerdahl's balsa raft, the 'Kon-Tiki'. He was a Norwegian explorer who tried to discover the possible routes that the early South American Indians followed as they drifted across the Pacific Ocean before colonising the many scattered islands. Heyerdahl and his raft sailed for one hundred and one days with the prevailing currents and winds, originally I think from Callao in Peru, over four thousand miles to the Tuamotu Islands of Polynesia. Since I knew that otters were...."

"....great wanderers and shy of man," announced Olivia excitedly from deep in her pillows, "I've heard you say that frequently about otters."

"....well that's why I called them Kon and Tiki, after the wanderings of the raft, but let me return to the story," I insisted, "or you'll be asleep before I've finished. The first interview between the presenter Joan Bakewell and the Travers' was completed successfully. Then during a break, the cameras were moved to different positions to cover Tiki and me, and Miss Bakewell. After being 'counted in', she started the interview by introducing me and asking me to comment on her first question."

"Which was?," asked Olivia impatiently.

She began, "Hunting has caused the decline of the otter...."

"Well that's not true for a start, and anyway hunting has been banned," Olivia protested.

"It has now, but don't forget, this was 1967. Sadly many people still took pleasure in the sport then. So I replied by saying what she had suggested was not strictly true. I added that although hunting had naturally had a severe effect, the important point to realise was that it was on an already greatly reduced

135

population, which was still continuing to suffer from the after-effects of chemical sprays."

"Good for you; so what did she say then?"

"She didn't say anything. She just stood up, obviously stopping the interview, and walked off across the studio."

"She did what?" Olivia had now pulled herself out from underneath her duvet in amazement.

"The floor director called 'cut' and I was left sitting there. He immediately came to sympathise. By the way, his name was Mike Appleton, the elder brother of Tim. Tim was working for me at the time in my wildlife park at Westbury-on-Trym, in Bristol. Tim had come with me to Cornwall to collect some of the guillemots and razorbills which had been washed ashore heavily oiled after the *Torrey Canyon* disaster. He had worked at the Wildfowl Trust and thirty years later, is still much involved in wildlife conservation. Nowadays he directs a project to establish the osprey as a breeding bird in the heart of England at Rutland Water. Osprey's are large fish-eating hawks...."

"I've seen a film about them!"

"The RSPB have over many years encouraged ospreys to breed in increasing numbers on the islands of several fresh-water lochs in Scotland. Indeed some of the lochs are now nationally important nature reserves. But back to my story. Tim's brother, Mike, told me to sit tight and continue as I had started, but warned me that Miss Bakewell, having now consulted with a male companion or researcher, call him what you will, would probably restart the interview by repeating my first statement; ie 'of course, most people think that hunting has caused the decline of the otter, but that's not strictly true; it's now known that chemical sprays, or the after-effects of their use, have played a major contribution' etcetera, etcetera."

"Did she really say all that?" Olivia was now quite indignant.

"Almost to the word, but instead she preceded the second part, about chemical sprays with the words, 'recent research has told us'."

"What did you do?"

"Well, I gave even more precise details in my response than either she or the 'researcher' could have known, to illustrate the various points. However, she had taken away the main plank of my answer, had stolen my thunder, if you like."

"That was pretty cheeky," Olivia's tone was one of disappointment.

"Some people, Olivia, can't bear to be out of control of a situation; she could hardly believe that her researcher had got his facts wrong and therefore thought, wrongly, that the viewers might see her in a poor light. All very feeble really. When she stalked off the set, I remember Bill Travers just raising his eyebrows and smiling. You should watch the film, 'Ring of Bright Water' again, and look out for that same quizzical look. In the studio at the time it was exactly the appropriate comment. Come on, bedtime now," I whispered," "talk to you some more tomorrow night. Then we'll try and get close to finishing this chapter, shall we?"

The following evening Olivia and I continued.

"I think I know another of the stories you're going to tell about me and Storm," observed Olivia rather pointedly; "I hope when it is written that people won't laugh at me."

"Would I do such a thing?" I responded lazily, but at the same time grinning rather mischievously. "You must remember that we could both recall several occasions when we have worked together with Storm and nothing untoward has happened, but just occasionally...."

".... just occasionally I have put my foot in it."

"Tell me," I enquired "which incident am I going to talk about?" I tried to keep up my expression of innocence, but felt sure I knew which story she would choose.

"How about when my glove puppet Sweep was drowned by Storm? It is, isn't it?" groaned Olivia, before I had time to comment.

I sensed that, frustrated as she was, Olivia was rather pleased that I was going to feature this particular incident.

"Tell me what you're going to put, and I will correct the facts," continued Olivia sarcastically, reminding me, as Helen often does, that I was likely to muddle the details. I never tell them but I do it deliberately!

"A private production company, *Wildcard Films* of Dartmouth in South Devon, had called to say that they were making a series of half-hour television programmes, in which people involved with unusual wildlife species and domestic animals and birds would be interviewed about their work by a former BBC television personality, Robert Robinson. He is well remembered for chairing 'Call my Bluff' for many years on BBC2."

"It seems I am always at school when a film crew arrives," shrugged Olivia, displaying less than her usual interest.

"Remember Robert Robinson had previously visited us on a reconnaissance trip. Then it had been a very wet and cold winter's day, and he had been excited seeing Storm quietly asleep in her inner den; we were living in north Somerset in those days and he had subsequently travelled further south on the M5 to his destination."

"So he was aware of Storm's set-up, how you would bring her regularly outside into my garden area to play."

"Absolutely, but on the morning of filming he wanted to conduct the first interview with Storm inside the inner den where she slept. Of course this meant bringing in the film cameraman, the sound recordist and their equipment too. The crew were ready but Robert Robinson was late. I was anxious not to lose the element of surprise with Storm since, as you know, she's brilliant when investigating somebody or something strange for the very first time. However, within minutes of his arrival he was ready to follow me inside.

"We'll film and tape the interview as it happens," he said. "If you and I try to react quite naturally and spontaneously to what Storm does, or does not do, I'll cut and edit the footage later with my director, Kevin Crooks."

"Sounds pretty straightforward."

"He was remarkably confident for someone from the world of 'showbiz', and who wasn't 'animally' so to speak. Not nervous at all. Both the interview and Storm were going well...."

"Until........ "

"Until nothing really," I smiled and almost gave the game away. "But you will remember how, whenever you and I used to sit with our backs upright against the wall of her den with our knees drawn up against our chests, Storm would start to explore us eagerly. Well, having done exactly that, she then proceeded to climb up into Robert Robertson's lap. Unfortunately I'd forgotten to mention to him about Storm and hats."

"Really?" Olivia's eyes nearly popped out of her head. "Daddy is a dummer!"

"Thank you, there's no need to make a meal of it."

"You always do with me!"

"I had mentioned to him previously to stay absolutely still at all times however close she came, and this he did, However moments later Storm stretched up and started to pull at his cap."

138

"I suppose he tried to stop Storm taking it off altogether."

"He hung on to it with one hand, and asked me why she wanted his cap. I was telling him to let her take it and not to try and prevent her doing so since...."

"....since she would only pull it all the harder."

"When I said, without thinking, 'Storm just thinks it's a bit of roughage', he looked aghast as Storm scampered off."

"With his cap?"

"He responded dryly, 'Just a bit of roughage?' Goodness knows what Herbert Johnson of Bond Street would think, hearing that one of their exclusive country caps had been referred to in such a way. However, as he spoke, he was smiling. The interview was concluded ahead of schedule because of the successful pre-planning. This was the reason why, after ringing for permission, Mummy fetched you from Weare School. Robert Robinson was enthusiastic to record your relationship with Storm. I had explained how close you both were when he had previously called."

"I was nervous coming into the garden to be met by all those people," complained Olivia.

"Perhaps that was wrong of me; nevertheless you were soon on your swing and Storm was chasing you backwards and forwards."

"Do you remember she loved trying to catch the length of sash cord as it dragged across the grass? Do you think she thought it was an eel? She always joined in that game. When we first introduced her to my garden, I would drag the piece of rope around for her to pounce on it. It was just how you would teach a kitten to hunt."

"I'm sure there's a natural instinct to respond to movement, to immediately bite the cord, and it's interesting that whenever she thought she had mastered it, she would always drag it across the grass to her tank."

"And dunk it!" added Olivia enthusiastically, "I mean drown it as if to finally finish it off. Mind you, she always did that with the slugs, and anything else she thought she had found first."

"She knew our tone of voice too. When we called her to give something up, or the more we called her name, the more she turned her head in on herself, and made it virtually impossible to prise anything away from her."

"She'd chitter in anger, and that morning she was doing so again when my filming had finished. Suddenly, when she thought no one was looking, she popped over to where my sweater was on the ground and stole poor Sweep. You feel almost as if it was deliberately done, that perhaps Sweep's presence was annoying her."

"Maybe she felt she was no longer the centre of attention, even possibly jealous in some way," I suggested.

"As I called Sweep, and you shouted Storm."

"No," I interrupted, "as I called Storm and you shouted Daddy! Daddy! very loudly."

"Well whatever, Storm bounced off even faster to her tank and dived underwater," Olivia continued. "My poor Sweep."

Olivia was still very saddened by the demise of one of her favourite 'fluffies', even though the story had been repeated many times to friends. Indeed, the recording involving Olivia had gone as well as the previous indoor shoot, with most of the sequences of Olivia on her swing with Storm in close attendance filmed at a distance of only a few feet. The camera on the tripod was set almost at ground level and both Olivia and Storm had been most effectively captured, particularly Storm swimming and playing in her tank with Olivia sitting alongside. So, for all intents and purposes, that was the successful end of proceedings. Luckily for all of us the various bits of equipment had not been immediately dismantled, but had been covered in various protective wrappings. It was over coffee and biscuits, when we were reappraising what had been successfully achieved with the filming, that suddenly our attention was not only drawn to Storm's antics, but also to Olivia's sudden and simultaneous cries of despair. Storm, thinking she had been ignored, was confining the hapless Sweep to a watery but temporary grave.

In an instant the cameraman had captured some completely unrehearsed footage. It was obvious that Storm was not going to give up her prize for some time. I felt sorry for Olivia, as did everyone else present, as rather despondently and with tears running down her face, she took her leave with Helen. The crew enjoyed one last look at Storm who was still floating lazily, but rather cockily, in her tank. Occasionally she completed a three hundred and sixty degree roll and the bedraggled Sweep would break the surface momentarily, clasped tightly between Storm's fore and rear legs.

Robert Robinson's final remark before he left for his next assignment was made with kindness and without malice. 'Sweep is just another piece of roughage in Storms eyes.' Happily, but much later, Sweep had made a complete recovery in the spin dryer!

"Are you leaving one of my favourite times when we were out with Storm until last?"

"Which one would that be?" I enquired. "Let me have a guess; there were several at Old Holt Farm with personalities and friends. Could it have been with Peter Symons for BBC Children's Television?"

"No, doing 'Star Pets' was good but the easiest and most fun, well everybody was just so relaxed, was your interview with John Nettles for 'Animal Passions' at the Tamar Otter Sanctuary. Do you remember it kept pouring with rain, and just when everybody thought it was going to be impossible to complete, it worked like a treat."

"That occasionally happens doesn't it, the luck goes with you. You're quite right. Everybody worked with no fuss and Ken and Carwyn contributed greatly. There were no bad vibes, and John Nettles was completely at ease with Storm and I was confident and relaxed. So the talk went well covering all that we had planned to discuss about the problems facing otters."

"Finally Ross Hoddinott took some lovely photographs, even in the pouring rain."

"Mind you, what other weather can you expect for north Cornwall in early December?" I observed.

"Do you remember I was sitting on John Nettles' knee and our chairs were steadily sinking into the wet ground?" Olivia's face was a picture.

In fact, Olivia was right. One particular photograph, pulled later from Ross's roll of film, captured the memory of working with many different delightful personalities, an enchanting daughter, and a unique British otter.

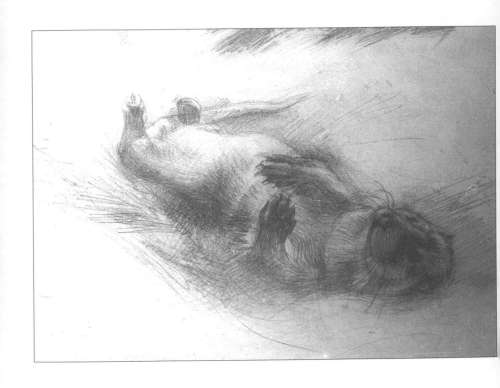

SEVEN

"WARWICK WAS NOW, UNDOUBTEDLY, HER FRIEND"

I was later than normal taking Storm her supper of ox-heart, liver and mackerel, and when I did enter her enclosure, I said I wanted to stay awhile before leaving her with her food.

"We need to talk at some length." I started rather abruptly. "You have accompanied me most times on my lectures and usually we've been able to return the same day, even though sometimes it has been late into the night."

"We were away for a while at last summer's Royal Welsh Show," interrupted Storm, "but then we had the vet's house where we could stay with your friends . So what's the problem?"

"I have just been speaking on the phone to Martha Holmes a senior producer from the BBC's Wildlife-on-One series; you will remember her, she was the producer for the underwater shots we tried in the fresh-water tank at Set Location in Avonmouth. Do you recall the cameraman, Stephen de Vere, discussing how he had over-wintered in Antarctica whilst filming for the Natural History Unit's 'Life in the Freezer' series?"

"But the tank shots didn't work out. Does she want to try again?"

"No, I think from our lengthy conversation she wants to use you to complete various location sequences, which are as yet unfinished and which they have been putting together over the past fifteen months or so."

"Where does she intend to do all this?" Storm interrupted.

"Well that's really why I need to talk to you. I think ideally it's down to us to choose an area where we would have several potential venues."

"Did she tell you exactly the situations she wants to recreate?"

"It appears that for the programme to be concluded successfully she needs extra footage of an otter exploring its territory, swimming in shallow water, and perhaps then shaking

143

itself dry from the head and shoulders on some prominent rock mid-stream. Other pictures would be it foraging for and locating food, fresh-water crayfish or eels maybe, and finally coming ashore to typically mark its territory."

"Go on say it, you mean 'sprainting'," interrupted Storm mischievously.

"Yes okay, 'sprainting' and snuffling about in a ditch or a wet drain for frogs just as wild otters would do close to any main water course on their territory. And, wait for it, everything in close up!" I added finally and rather sarcastically.

"But of course. However, I reckon I could do all that," said Storm rather excitedly, "especially as I prefer to be out of doors. By the way, what *were* all those strange smells in that warehouse place?"

"They came from aerosol sprays that the crew were using to cover up blemishes on the set."

"They were something else and they irritated my nostrils and my eyes. Then there was the noise from the pumps as they tried to recreate the rivers running water and...."

"Anyway," I continued, trying not to let Storm become too carried away, "returning to the phone call, I gather it is now appreciated how difficult it can be to predict where wild otters live since the animals are frequently on the move within their very large territories. Remember your mother, she never seemed to delay in one place for too long. Secondly, that it is even more impossible to track an otter's precise movements at dusk and dawn, and therefore to follow its very private and personal life. Somehow the cameramen have to complete those sequences they have already obtained, and preferably at close quarters. So yes, they do need you, and I agree I reckon you could do it, and very well too," I concluded.

There was a slight pause and then Storm continued.

"Couldn't your friend Ken Hill at the Tamar Otter Sanctuary help? Surely between you could find enough suitable locations close to hand where I could be filmed. I wouldn't mind staying overnight there for a spell. I would feel quite at home being close to Pebble, Ripple and Blackthorn again. In fact, it would be great, and I could catch up with all their news. Go on, ask him, please," Storm concluded excitedly.

"You know.... that's some idea! I will phone Ken at his home on Dartmoor and arrange to visit North Petherwin as soon as possible. We'll work *something* out. Well done!"

I gave Storm her food, and checked her enclosure. As always, I double-locked her door and immediately started contemplating in detail how best I could build upon Storm's brilliant idea. I would definitely be ringing Ken later that evening.

A few days later I was in north Cornwall to plan both my role and that of Storm in the forthcoming film project. I had enjoyed a close friendship with Ken ever since he had come from Norfolk. He had worked at the Great Witchingham collection of Philip Wayre since 1978 and had gathered his extensive knowledge both from his own deep interest in the countryside and from working alongside another close friend of mine, Roy Grout. Roy had joined the staff when I was working as Mr Wayre's 'pupil' in 1961 and 1962 before I left Norfolk to go university. Roy was a loyal stalwart at both the Norfolk Wildlife Park and the Otter Trust for over twenty years, overseeing the first breeding successes of many rare species of animals and birds in both collections. But both he and Ken had departed for different personal reasons within months of each other in 1985. Now Ken already had over ten years under his belt establishing the Otter Trust's reserve and sanctuary on the Devon/Cornwall border.

Ken's home was a few miles from the wild coastal marshes at Salthouse. It was from there in December 1966 that I had collected my first orphaned otter cub and from where this ongoing and magical story had begun. A few miles along the coast Philip Wayre, the founder of The Otter Trust, to whom Helen and I had been donating cubs bred in our family group for many years for the Trust's release programme, had also seen his first wild otter emerging before him in a creek on the Stiffkey Marshes in the 1930s. As I sat down in the North Petherwin tearoom for what promised to be a long session, I could'nt help wondering again how that area of remote coast had remarkably brought all three of us, and our love for wildfowl and otters in particular, together. Now between us or rather perhaps because of us, we could piece together yet another important chapter in the otter's tale. The making of the Wildlife-on-One film for millions to view would hopefully contribute to the continuing and eventual recovery of otters in the wild in these islands.

I was looking into the sanctuary where the far boundary was formed by the meandering Boleswater Brook, and also into a small grass paddock which was flanked by the wild wood, home to the fallow and muntjac deer. Below lay the four British otter pens in which the original trio of otters had arrived from East Anglia with Ken. Taw the dog otter had fathered twenty-three cubs through Tavy and Wensum, a quite remarkable bonding, the success due as much, no doubt, to Ken's constant care with them.

Now Taw and Tavy were at peace together beneath one of the goat willows close to the largest and most natural pond created for the wildfowl, and three of my otters, close friends of Storm, had been introduced to continue the marvellously productive Tamar breeding line. Blackthorn had been equally successful within our family group in Somerset with a lovely bitch otter called Willow; she had reared eleven of his cubs and most had gone to Earsham to support the Otter Trust's release programme. Now sadly Blackthorn had been recently widowed, and it was planned that he should spend his latter years with the ageing Wensum. I found it remarkable that neither Tavy or Wensum had bred before coming to Cornwall. I wondered whether Ripple and Pebble, both of whom had yet to breed too and who were as different as chalk and cheese in character and looks, would also provide the source of many more cubs.

This was a lovely environment for the otters, and I could understand how Storm would immediately relax here, especially since she would be able to chatter with some of her pals who would be just across the paddock at night. It was in this atmosphere that I was soon thinking seriously about the exciting filming programme which might lie ahead.

Since that initial telephone call I had now spoken at length with our on location producer, Sarah Byatt. Sarah had recently returned from South America and in particular the River Amazon Basin. As an assistant director she had successfully completed 'Spirits of the Jaguar', which had been edited into four fifty minute episodes for a forthcoming 'The Natural World' on BBC2. Now her remit from Martha Holmes was to direct the final but vital location shots with Storm for the otter programme. She was favouring venues in and around the Bristol area, close to the Natural History Unit, but the more I talked with Ken that lunchtime the more convinced I became that for many reasons the Tamar Sanctuary should become our base.

"First let's talk about possible locations close at hand," I volunteered.

Initially my thoughts concerned the areas around the largest natural lake at the lower end of the sanctuary. It was here that the small flock of striking white lesser snow geese always seemed to be the boss family around. There was an extensive and easily separable wild area, overgrown with alder and willow, mostly mature and shortly to be coppiced. The lower moss-covered limbs were almost lost amongst clumps of tussocky grass and deep rush cover. Various species of wild water birds including kingfisher and snipe were to be found here all year round. During the summer, swallows and house martins had been busy dipping in low over the surface of the water from dawn to dusk to snatch the gnats and midges. Their youngsters eagerly awaited the fruits of their hunting in the outbuildings or under the eaves of the nearby farmhouse. Indeed one pair of bold swallow parents regularly brought off at least two broods a summer from a nest that was only just above head height in one of the otter observation huts. Thousands of visitors would pass through, unaware that three or four pairs of eyes were watching their every move. The otter family did not escape their attentions either.

On frosty winter mornings when Ken or his assistant Carwyn carried out their early rounds, an occasional teal or shoveler would spring from the water's edge amongst the clumps of bog cotton grass. In the early afternoon when the large numbers of resident wildfowl were being fed for the second time in the day at that time of year, it was quite common to have a flock of up to fifty yellow-hammers busy searching for the grains, the birds almost being crushed amongst the webbed feet of the greylag and barnacle geese. These finches, increasingly rare, are victims of all that is wrong nowadays in the environment from the results of modern and mechanised farming practices. The flock was always more prominent in the harshest days of January and February, with Ken maintaining that it was a better guide to approaching spring than the early nesting mallard or the first arrivals of individual swallows; whilst the yellow-hammers still "flocked" then winter was still with us and it would often be well into April, and certainly after the traditional Easter holiday weekend before they dispersed with their chosen mates to their summer nesting sites.

"You could easily enclose an area there for filming," was Ken's response, "and there would be no permanent damage to the reedbed. In any case the vegetation continues to die right back during the autumn, and then with the spring growth no one will realise you have been there. You have easy access to this marsh too," he added, "and that's also going to be very important for bringing Storm's travelling crate in and out."

Indeed Ken was absolutely right. It was vital to be able to transport Storm without undue fuss into the different locations. It was always my plan to have a small island, or area of bank available within all the penned filming areas that might be chosen, so that Storm could exit the crate onto firm ground. Immediately adjacent would be her sprainting mat. Storm's customary pattern of behaviour was to mark this heavy duty rubber mat instantly before setting off to explore any new area. Ideally, once the crate was removed so as not to hinder filming, the mat would remain, and if necessary be hidden under some extra vegetation. When eventually she became bored or tired she would, inevitably, head back directly to her original sprainting point.

In addition, and as a temporary move in order to give her a greater feeling of familiarity, I planned to leave my old fur-lined waterproof jacket on the ground as well. On cold evenings I had begun deliberately to entrust the coat to her so that she could become accustomed to my body scent. I quickly gathered that she loved to return to lie in the soft lining where she would roll and rub, instantly drying herself and at the same time stimulating her own coat as well. Finally when Sarah the director decided that enough footage was in the can for that particular shoot, and that the sequence could therefore be concluded, then the travelling crate with its inviting and comforting dry straw bed, towels and familiar smells could be repositioned. Then nine times out of ten Storm would be only too glad to climb back in and settle down.

"Of course," Ken continued, "you can always overnight here as well. At the moment in the barn where we work and prepare the food for all the animals and birds in the collection, we have an unoccupied emergency pen. Her travelling box will fit inside that pen, and, whenever or wherever she is required, all you will have to do is to 'crate' her, load her into the van which, in turn, can be parked alongside. Then away you go."

"And reverse the process on our return," I interrupted, "couldn't be better in fact."

"Finally there will be no problem with storing the small amount of food you will need. I know you keep her on a specialist diet but we have a couple of large freezers on hand and therefore plenty of space is available. There are also bound to be several potential locations we can find for filming, given the many streams and rivers close to here. I will give that some immediate thought too. I am reckoning this is by far the best place overall, so it's up to you to persuade Sarah!"

"We are definitely stringing this together," I added excitedly, "the only remaining problem I can foresee is that I shall need a full-time assistant. I must be able to keep a constant check on an enclosure's boundaries during filming, especially the two lengths through which the river's waters will be flowing. One particular problem to avoid is the fence being lifted off the bed of the river, and Storm being able to slip through underwater and out of sight aided by the strong current. The BBC's construction teams will set up and I have already met with Dave Brockman in Bristol. He will be in charge of the construction of the first two pens, wherever they will be, in Somerset or around here. However, during filming, total responsibility for the safety of Storm always lies entirely with me, and English Nature insists on that. Do you think a young person who might actually want to help could be that young wildlife photographer of the year? I am sure he lives somewhere near here. I cannot think of his name, but I can see now his outstanding award winning picture of mute swans in a recent BBC Wildlife magazine."

"Lately he has been coming into the sanctuary here, taking many shots of the otters and of the fallow deer in the wild wood to enhance his portfolio. I cannot place his name either right now, but I will keep an eye open for him and will mention to Pat Terry, our manageress in the gatehut, that you want to speak to him."

"I suppose Carwyn could always help, too," I suggested, thinking of Ken's assistant.

"On his days off of course, and if you are actually filming in the park, I am sure I could spare him for an hour or two. Anyway he would like to help; he is very keen and practical too, it would be right up his street."

"Your visitors will probably be very interested in what is going on as well, especially if when they leave they know they may well see one of the sequences again one evening next year on BBC1."

"Yes that's true. They will reminisce, particularly if Carwyn has updated them with all the latest information at one of his lively feeding sessions with the otters. They will talk to their friends about the various characters they've seen so close at hand and about the work of the Otter Trust and its release programme. It will be good publicity for us."

By now I was as clear in my mind, as was Ken, that Tamar was by far and away the best base from which to work. As I left the Sanctuary long after its closing time, having further explored the marsh as a potential filming enclosure, the valley was bathed in the intense yellow sunshine so typical of a late autumn evening here in Cornwall. What if Storm could be filmed in that light? Was it a good omen for the days ahead? Excitedly I headed home to West Penwith and to Helen and Olivia.

Why otters swim under water but close to the surface

Diagram 1

If you hold a straight stick so that parts of the stick are under water and you look at the stick from above the water, the stick appears to bend or kink as it enters the water. Of course, the stick does not really bend. It just appears to do so. Diagram 1 illustrates the effect, which is an example of an optical phenomenon called refraction. Refraction occurs because the air and the water have different values of an optical property called the refractive index. (see page 169)

© Alan Duncan – O'Connor, Australia

At a planning meeting at the BBC in Clifton Bristol, Sarah had agreed to filming in north Cornwall and in order not to lose any more time, she had immediately visited, researched and chosen some different locations. The first was to be downstream of Waterloo Bridge within two miles of the Sanctuary. Here the River Ottery ran from Ham Mill to Werrington before joining the Tamar at Week St Mary. I was travelling from Somerset very early in the morning and everything I needed for the next fortnight was on board.

Ross Hoddinott, the cameraman, whom Ken and I were previously trying to identify, had been located, and had agreed to 'assist' and whilst on location to take some stills photos if it were at all possible. The indoor pen at Tamar was ready for overnighting, and I had to be on location with Storm early in the afternoon. It was all systems go.

"Go out and enjoy yourself," I said to Storm as I travelled from north Somerset and left the M5 heading southwest, and started the second part of our journey on the A30 to Okehampton, Launceston and thence to North Petherwin. "Remember there is no need to be frightened, you are not going to be asked to do anything impossible. Explore the various enclosures in your own time and enjoy the sensation of the fast running water. It should be great fun."

"I have been trying to imagine it," Storm replied. "I have been chatting to Cider at night".

"What did he say? He's done various filming with me over the years. I once travelled through the night with him to, of all places, the Cafè Royal in London, in order to help launch a book on the countryside."

"Yes, he told me. But that was very much an indoors situation in completely artificial surroundings. You had Helen with you, a man Olivia calls Uncle Bill plus your lady vet Penny Robinson, and you came back later the same day. These will all be different places and with strange people. I am bound to be nervous."

Storm was letting her imagination run away with her, and I realised that I needed to change her line of thought quickly to reassure her.

"Please don't worry. It will work out, you'll see, and when I have left you at night, you will have Ripple and company to talk to," I added.

"Yes I know, and come to think of it, I must tell you some of Cider's stories about his time living with you. He chatted about some of his closest otter friends,"

"That would be Willow for certain," I interrupted,

"Oh yes Willow, and Tigger who was always arguing with him. But he also went as far back as his time at the Otter Trust at Earsham. It seems his mother had no milk and so, as a little boy, he was bottle-fed along with his brother Perry. They were both very friendly with a golden labrador called Sam, weren't they?"

"Yes that's right, and I'd love to hear Cider's recollections too. Perhaps you will recall some of them for me when we are filming.

There's bound to be times when the weather is poor or when the light has gone flat."

"Or there will be a tractor working nearby and the noise will drown everything," said Storm enthusiastically, thinking that would also give her the time to chatter to Ross and myself. At that moment I did not have the heart to tell her that filming would continue given most outside interruptions, so long as the light was good. Appropriate sounds could either be deleted, or dubbed in, later. So I consoled her for the moment.

"There could well be the odd military helicopter overhead on exercise," I added, "particularly if Sarah has chosen any locations on the remoter parts of Bodmin Moor. Anyway, for the moment I must concentrate on the road. You will be alright, you'll see. I promise you will have experienced most of the noises many times before."

Waterloo Bridge was not five minutes drive from our base. I had met with Ross for the first time, and had introduced him to Storm, and very soon he and I were inspecting the first enclosure that had been strung across the River Ottery. Our first and most important task, as it was to be at every other location, was to check the security of the boundary fences, which the Unit's construction team had erected. There were no problems. Dave Brockman had remembered all the various safety details, and it was not long before Ross and I were carrying Storm the half mile or so in her travelling crate to the river bank.

Final preparations were made and with Warwick Sloss, the cameraman, in position with his equipment, the travelling crate was finally lifted in and the door was opened. At long last the first session was under way and all we could do now was to sit back and wait for Storm to exit and explore.

Eventually, after about half an hour, Storm left her crate and having immediately sprainted, proceeded to explore the perimeter of the pen. I stood on the high river banks which formed two of the boundaries. It was an ideal spot for keeping an eye on Storm's whereabouts on land, and more particularly her movements in the crystal clear waters of the Ottery. All went well, with Ross keeping a watching brief from the outer boundary fence on the downstream flank. It was towards here that Storm was most frequently being carried by the strong current, and she was tending to spend most of her time upending and exploring. I was well out of camera range but still inside the enclosure. Occasionally Storm worked her way upstream, delaying as she explored the larger upstanding rocks and struggling from time to time against the river's flow. I was encouraging her to linger by dropping some of her spraint into the weed and moss growing over the exact boulders that Warwick had planned to highlight. Storm often paused, head raised, sniffing on the wind, just as a truly wild otter would hesitate when first coming across the particular scent of another individual. Delightfully, Storm repeated this behaviour pattern several times over nearly three quarters of an hour, surely giving Warwick, who had changed position and angle frequently, several chances for stunning head-on silhouette pictures. Eventually, she would slide away into the deeper waters which were streaming past the rounded boulders. The thumb's-up sign, which was coming ever more frequently to Sarah from Warwick, suggested the footage was good.

The second but equally vital part of Storm's first day on location was her introduction to the sleeping quarters that Ken and Carwyn had carefully prepared, and which was going to be her home for the next few days.

"That went very well this afternoon" I said to her, as Ross and I reloaded the travelling crate into the van.

"I really enjoyed myself, and it was so peaceful on the river with the sound of the running water."

"There was no need to feel nervous, was there?" I interrupted. "You were fine; there was no pressure on you and the camera crew took their time. Now we will organise a good night for you and take it from there tomorrow."

Before Ross and I actually lifted her travelling crate into the indoor enclosure, we filled her cold water tank and set out the straw bales on which were laid Storm's favourite towels and her dishes of food. Then it was time to leave Storm to settle and to explore her second strange environment in one day.

Ross left for Bude excited he had completed his first afternoon's work, although he had not managed to take any stilis photos. The light had been very good at times, but with the overhanging trees only just beginning to show signs of shedding their leaf cover in any quantity, the intermittent patterns of brightness and shade proved frustrating and would again over the following days not just for Ross, but more importantly for Warwick.

Now it was time for me to return home. Finally I crept into Storm's pen and sat quietly close to her. She had been out and sprainted, had rubbed herself dry and was now stretched out upside down inside the crate.

"Are you happy"? I enquired.

"Fine," came the sleepy reply; "I am going to lie up awhile, I might fancy my food later."

"Everything you need is in place" I added. "You will remember that Ken and Carwyn will still be preparing the evening meals for their otters; I am sure they will switch off Radio Five Live when they lock up!" I joked.

"I am used to Sybil Roscoe and John Inverdale when I'm travelling with you in the van," I heard her say.

"You will probably hear your otter friends talking later tonight, so it will be quite exciting for you."

There was no reply. A quick glance indicated that Storm's eyes were shut and she was asleep with her dreams. It was only then that I realised I had forgotten to remind her of the new and strange noises she might hear that night. More than most otters she was accustomed to a greater variety of sounds living as she did in her artificial world. Later, and for the first time, she might well hear the fallow bucks arguing amongst themselves over their chosen does, or the courting eagle owls close by in the wild wood, or from afar even the drake eiders 'whooing' to their spouses on the main pool. There was every likelyhood too, that there would be yet another family squabble between the families of greylag and barnacle geese. I remembered that several of the barnies in the flock were originally my birds, so I was comforted knowing that, if Storm had seen a creature or heard a sound just the once, then she never forgot its identity or its significance.

As far as I knew there had only been one occasion when Storm did not immediately cope. When she was growing up in her first summer in north Somerset, Olivia and I would spend an hour or two most evenings playing in the back garden with her. On one occasion Olivia suddenly spotted a little owl above us, perched on the ridge of the single storey shippen. The owl could not work out exactly what Storm was as she darted backwards and forwards in the long grass, going to and from her tank and chasing the sash cord being dragged across the grass by Olivia from her swing.

Olivia and I watched spellbound as the little owl, a female, drew herself up to her largest size in the typical defence posture. She bobbed and weaved continuously as Storm continued to play below her, and Storm had no idea she was being watched either.

Suddenly the owl let fly with an aggressive bark. On every other occasion previously when a noise had startled Storm as, for instance, when she came home from Roger and Wendy Lee the first time and heard the metal gates clanging in the farmyard opposite, or when the tractors had changed down a couple of gears as they approached the lane close to her sleeping quarters, with their trailers laden with freshly-cut silage, she would hesitate. Within moments however she would continue unconcerned. But that night she instantly froze in fear and remained rigidly still for some time. It was as if the little owl's alarm 'yap' had triggered a response which was set in her mind from time immemorial. It was clear that no mother otter would have taught her to cope with that; the reaction hadto be born out of an instinct inherent over many tens of generations. Wherever the little owl might have been, her alarm call would have had the same affect on every neighbouring wild creature. The female

155

mallard, in the midst of idle chatter, would have let go a deeper 'quack', and every other bird, not just every other duck, would have responded with its own particular alarm call.

I was thrilled that Olivia, who had first spotted the owl, was able to record with me for all time a remarkable behavioural phenomenon within the 'natural world'.

So I guessed that tonight the idle chattering and bickering of the geese would in fact be a source of comfort rather than of fear for Storm.

Carwyn had kindly pinned a welcoming sign on the door of Storm's pen. There was a silver cardboard star and a large stick-on pink bow with the accompanying words, 'Storm's dressing room'; and in the half light I could still see the white patch on Storm's right upper lip as she snored quietly.

Now I could leave comfortably for home, with the first two sessions successfully completed.

Day two saw our first afternoon's work in the reedbed, which Ken and I thought would prove a most suitable and rewarding location. The construction team had moved on to prepare another location away from base whilst Sarah and Warwick had quietly enclosed a section of the marsh in the sanctuary during the morning. They had specifically picked out a clump of low-lying and partially fractured limbs of a mature willow. They were well covered in moss, and Storm would alternately contrast with or fade into the background. It would be a most attractive sequence, particularly shot in close-up. I had placed 'spots' of Storm's spraint to give her a confident start, and having emerged from her travelling crate, she would hopefully pause and investigate with Warwick, all the time positioned no more than a few feet away.

However, Storm was exhausted from the travelling and filming of the previous day. I moved the vehicle as close as possible to the proposed location, but I already knew it would be a matter of having to lift her out for any further activity on her part.

"Who were those strangers looking in at me a few moments ago?" she asked wearily.

"They were a couple who regularly holiday in this area of north Cornwall and always make a point of coming to see the otters here. The lady recognised me. I often used to go to the Yeo Moor

Junior and Infants' Schools in Clevedon in north Somerset where she was teaching, to present lectures on conservation to the youngsters. She made herself known, and I explained what we were doing here. They asked if they might see you. I hope you didn't mind."

"No, not really, but you realise I am very tired. I did not sleep much last night with all the strange bumps and noises in the night. I tell you there was one helluva racket coming from the other otters. I reckon there was something very strange going on. I must tell you about it later. Anyway, what's planned for today?"

"Sarah wants you in the reedbed, and Warwick will be tight in with the camera. I notice you are already getting on well with him. Just take your time."

With that Storm curled round on herself again; and I wondered if she realised that Ross and I had already carried the crate into position.

Storm did take her time too, so eventually I lifted her clear. However, although disappointed at having to 'work', she soon started investigating as planned. Everything was peaceful; Warwick had discovered a late-nesting woodpigeon in the upper branches of a willow directly above his chosen camera position. But even with Warwick and Storm so close, the bird persisted in sitting tight and completely ignored the proceedings below her.

Suddenly the tranquility was shattered. I could not believe that just outside the sanctuary's perimeter fence, a Cornwall County Council tractor had started trimming the roadside hedgerow, slashing all and sundry before it. As it crawled slowly uphill, the blades accelerated rapidly whenever they grated into the thicker branches and the more resistant wood. Then having turned at the top of the hill by completing what seemed to be the fastest and noisiest three point turn possible, the driver raced back to start the destruction at a different angle and level all over again. All this was happening no more than 50 metres away from us. By the time Sarah could firstly leave the quagmire of the reedbed, and secondly the sanctuary itself, in order to confront the operator and request him to move elsewhere, Storm naturally had become very frightened indeed. The driver had been completely unaware of us, the noise had been horrific and the damage had been done.

The following afternoon we attempted the reedbed sequence again, this time in a perfectly peaceful atmosphere. The woodpigeon was still aloft, brooding quietly, having endured the

County Council blitz too. There was the same mixture of dappled light, but Storm was much more active, having benefited from a restful second night. She quietly but systematically explored and paused, and with Warwick changing his camera position just a couple of times, the sequences were easily obtained. Two hours later Storm was back in the barn with her food for the night, and the second of two totally contrasting sequences had been achieved.

I was quietly pleased and I believed Sarah and Warwick were beginning to warm to Storm's particular character. They were becoming aware of Storm's personal ways of approaching what were, for her, very strange and alien situations.

During the following days, and as was to be expected now in late October, there were constant interruptions for poor weather, and further delays because it was not always easy to find a location which overcame the more prohibiting factors. Heavy overnight rain meant a location deemed suitable the previous evening could lose its island or area of dry ground after our initial reconnaissance and survey of the construction team's work. So the vital need for an easy release and recapture of Storm was lost through the rapid, almost instant, increase in water levels. The same rise in depth also meant that any restrictive fencing which had been erected was likely to give way under the extra force of the flow. It was becoming apparent that we might soon have to rely on the streams running off the peat moors. At least the water would tend to stay clear rather than become discoloured. Also important was the continual need to be able to park our relevant vehicles close to any location, so that both Warwick and Storm could either enter or leave rapidly. These problems were causing some concern for us but most particularly for Sarah.

However, we then spent two successful days at Bathpool Bridge close by the Launceston to Liskeard road. Here was a stretch of the River Lynher that met all of our requirements. There was an easy approach to the river by way of a cattle drinking access which was close to the arched stone packhorse bridge. It was a gently flowing river holding its level even after rain, and the assembled enclosure contained different environments, giving Sarah and Warwick a variety of shots. Finally one boundary was created by a partially walled steep bank to the river, ideal for me to patrol and monitor Storm's activities. I could remain unseen behind the trunks of several elm trees, and therefore Storm was not distracted by the need for either Ross or me to be close in order to be constantly vigilant.

There was no doubt that both Storm and the whole team relaxed when in more favourable surroundings. Carwyn had joined us here, and he was used, very successfully, as the newcomer who attracted Storm's attention at critical moments. Like Warwick previously, he felt immediately at home with her, and with Storm sensing his friendliness, Carwyn stayed in the enclosure throughout the shoot. It was the light factor that was now all important. Obviously we needed the best to coincide with the periods of Storm's greatest interest and activity in her surroundings. Although Ross and I were some distance from the proceedings, time and again we would hear Warwick's short but emphatic remarks to his director Sarah, reminding her that the light had gone flat again.

During the time spent there much was achieved, with little outside interference save for the occasional curious villager who delayed on the bridge whilst walking the dog. One or two particular dogs had many more walks than was customary over those two days! Storm continued to build her rapport with Warwick; I guessed Ross had obtained some good stills too, judging by the occasional gesture to me from his station downstream. It was so peaceful that I was able to look away from time to time to watch for dippers on whose territory we had apparently strayed.

Sarah then moved the filming onto the peat streams. The prime location was near Bolventor; the pens were smaller, and the water deeper and faster flowing. There was the feeling, which was perhaps vital in some way, of a wilder, more remote 'ottery' landscape. For us this was borne out by the occasional and apparently languid sortie of a buzzard overhead, and the distant 'kronking' of some belligerent raven on the far skyline. The drawback for Storm was that the air temperatures were appreciably down. The nip of autumn was quite noticeable on the higher moors, and accordingly the water was much colder. Storm was soon heading back to the inner woollen lining of my upturned weather coat after staying immersed for considerably shorter periods. However, I knew again that much was achieved overall, despite one afternoon's work being severely cut short after we had been 'buzzed' by a SWEB helicopter. Its occupants were intrigued to understand why half a dozen people should be standing in a remote stream in the middle of Bodmin Moor. Obviously they never spotted Storm, indeed we were lucky to keep her within the penned enclosure. I was not to know at the time that this dramatic experience was to prove invaluable for Storm in a future filming project.

Daily now the weather was less kind and the light levels were steadily deteriorating. Constant low pressure off the western Atlantic meant grey skies, frequent periods of drizzle accompanied by banks of persistent mist. Much of what Sarah and Warwick had set out to achieve was already 'in the can', but there was one more planned sequence to be attempted in the sanctuary. When completed, there would be one final day for returning onto the moors.

Earlier in the summer, a previous camera crew from the Unit had travelled to the island of Lewis in the Outer Hebrides to record the reintroduction of an otter into the wild. When originally rescued, it was found to have been injured, and as it was already a mature individual feeding for itself, it was quite wild. The eventual release from its travelling crate after the recovery period was not going to be easily obtained. Not surprisingly, it departed for the nearby loch shore at some speed! Sarah reconstructed the release crate and had decided to position it on the closely mown grass of the sanctuary paddock which was grazed by the family group of barnacle geese. She hoped this would recreate the sheep-cropped turf of the Scottish islands. Storm would obviously exit at a more leisurely pace, so for her this filming was purely a technical exercise to be captured between the showers and the accompanying periods of poor light. Storm duly obliged without any great difficulty, and Warwick filmed from several different angles, including an overhead shot. A long length of sash-cord proved to be a stimulating aid for Storm to follow on several occasions, no doubt reminding her of the games played with Olivia during her first two summers in north Somerset. Carwyn gave his excellent imitation of the high pitched call of a rabbit to ensure Storm's ongoing interest, in what were, for her, rather boring circumstances compared to the previous few days.

Thus we came to the last possible day for working before contracts were ended. When we broke later that evening, no more filming would be undertaken, and Martha Holmes and the cutting editor would have to make the best of all the shots obtained both during our twelve days, from all the other locations visited and the weeks and months of filming previously undertaken. Again the weather did not bode well; on arrival at the sanctuary I was greeted by more heavy and squally showers and overcast conditions. I had travelled past many of our previously successful sites, and the peat streams were running strongly from Brown Willy and Rough Tor. As usual there was the additional ever-present problem of a blanket of thick grey mist.

Ross and I spent the morning discussing our recent and possible future times together with Storm. There were already potential bookings for Storm and myself to promote the otter conservation message. Warwick, talking with Ken and Carwyn, reminisced about previous assignments too but also wondered where the next few months' work might take him; and Sarah, ever the optimist, kept reporting every break, however temporary, in the cloud cover. Finishing this otter film had quickly followed her return from contributing seriously to the making of 'Jaguar' over the last two years, but now her forthcoming vacation was to take her back again to South America, this time more specifically to the Pampas of Southern Argentina.

"We might as well go for broke," was her sudden remark, "if we set up, we will be ready for any immediate break in the weather."

'Fortune favours the bold' was one of the phrases I mentioned to Ross as we left the A30 to head past Colliford Reservoir, with the weather still so poor we were unable to make out the far bank. The area was eerie and foreboding. This was Bodmin Moor at its most inhospitable .

Undaunted, Sarah asked us to help set up near another remote bridge she had discovered the previous evening. The rain was unrelenting and there seemed little point in continuing. We had been joined by Robin Duffy and his young son Neal. Robin worked for the Environment Agency and I gathered that it was he, who was able to confirm at short notice the ownership of the land where we hoped to film. This had been another of Sarah's anxieties throughout our time together. I remembered mentioning at our first planning meeting in Bristol that one of the criteria insisted upon by English Nature in the issuing of my yearly and ongoing licence to 'work' with Storm was my responsibility to ensure that, for whomsoever I was under contract, permission from the owner of the site must have been obtained before any filming commenced.

It was already mid-afternoon when suddenly the rain stopped.

Ten minutes later we were experiencing perhaps for one of the last times that year the wonderful yellow light that is so typical of late autumn in Cornwall. But, as two days earlier across the high moor at Bolventor, it was noticeably much colder than in the earlier days of our filming.

"This will be your last performance for 'Wildlife-on-One'," I whispered to Storm as Ross and I carried her in the crate to the water's edge close by the bridge. In a way it was quite amazing that the very last location that Sarah had discovered seemed to encompass the very best of all those previously used. There were pools of almost still deep water, alternating with shallow water running fast over a pebble bed, and finally pockets of reed and rush and the last of the summer weed and vegetation in quiet shallows, and where with much excitement Storm was later going to flush a resting small brown trout. There was a period of intense activity on Storm's part, and Warwick was certainly running up good footage, for he was soon changing magazines. He had positioned himself on the downstream side of our enclosure. Storm was frequently working up against the strong current, then after turning on the upstream boundary she would glide back towards him, stopping and pausing here and there, twisting and upending in the river flow, before finally drifting in between the legs of the camera tripod. After resting briefly against him, she would start the sequence all over again, before coming back to exactly the same spot. Warwick was now, undoubtedly, her friend.

An hour later and Storm was visibly tiring. I sensed, too, that the much colder temperatures of the fast running waters were now taking their toll. From time to time she was drawn ashore to where the familiar smells and warmth of her travelling crate awaited her. I called her back into mid-stream, but each time she was more reluctant, and on each occasion I saw the appealing look in her eyes, as she obviously wanted Sarah to finally call a halt.

It was another of Sarah's ideas that suddenly kept Storm going for a little while longer. Neal, who had been patiently watching proceedings next to his father all afternoon whilst at the same time standing remarkably still for one so young, was asked by her to run across the bridge. Storm immediately responded as he raced back and forth. She became even more excited when I asked him to call Storm by name. With his high pitched voice there was no doubt that Storm had immediate memories of Olivia and of playing happily with her in Olivia's nursery garden. Neal showed great persistence as he was encouraged to continue by his father. Storm had a new lease of life and Warwick was obviously concluding on 'a high' in terms of good sequences. Poor Storm, just as I could see her tiring for a second time, Neal's sister Rachel arrived from school and both youngsters proceeded to stimulate her yet again. This time I think Storm really did believe that Rachel was Olivia.

Although the light was still holding up well, the afternoon was fading fast. With the air temperatures dropping rapidly in clearing skies overhead, I was soon telling Sarah that we should now stop. Warwick was also indicating that he was into his last fifty feet of film and a matter of moments later I was lifting a very tired Storm into the quiet security of her travelling crate.

There were brief good-byes, talk of a job 'well done', promises of colour pictures of Storm to be sent to Neal and Rachel, followed by the fifteen mile return to North Petherwin. There we re-loaded for Somerset with final farewells from Storm to Ken, Carwyn and Ross, all of whom had been so helpful throughout.

I listened to Storm chattering to Pebble, Ripple and the big lad Blackthorn. It was good to know that, because of the filming they had all met up again. Storm in turn would take their particular otter news to Cider, a close friend of all four. Storm knew that Cider would never see them again; he had confided in her before she came on location that the place where all otters and their friends go was finally beckoning for him. No doubt Storm had passed on his love to his son and daughter, and he in turn would be reassured in his last days by the intimate messages of affection coming from Cornwall and which only pass between a father and his offspring.

So I gave Storm time. Ross must surely have been home near Bude before we departed, at last, towards a final unloading in north Somerset some four hours later, assisted by my friend Ashleigh Holtby. Storm slept throughout the entire journey, which was no surprise given her earlier exertions. I thought she would awaken when I bedded her down, and I planned to say 'well done'. However, by the light of my torch, I could see she was still upside down asleep, 'out for the count'. But even then I sensed she was fully aware of where she was, alongside Cider. Meanwhile I moved that close to Cider that I could clearly hear his gentle and peaceful snoring as well. I knelt over him and, with my fingers, I stroked the back of his head and neck, as I had done at least once every day since he had come from the Otter Trust in Suffolk all those years ago, to live with Helen and myself.

There was no doubt in my mind that those declarations of love from Tamar would be passed on to him by Storm much later in the still and quiet of the night.

"There he was curled up inside a large coil of heavy duty and oil-stained marine rope. An upturned clinker rowing boat which was almost completely covering him obviously protected him from the worst of the elements. He looked at me as if butter would not melt in his mouth. Unbelievably, he was no more than a few feet from the Bristol Channel and the open sea!"

"He had been out for how long?" asked Storm excitedly.

"That was his fourth night of freedom. You see, he had originally forced his way out on Christmas night. I had fed the family group earlier in the day and assumed that I had secured all the enclosures as normal.

"Surely all the doors were always triple-locked and there still was the extra safety of the lobby?" insisted Storm. As always when Storm's curiosity is fired, she never gave me time to finish what I was saying.

"Yes I know they are locked that way but you can always make mistakes you know," I added quickly. "In my rush to go home to Helen and Olivia to enjoy sharing the joy of Olivia opening her Christmas presents, I couldn't have fastened the bottom bolt. When I arrived early on Boxing Day morning to feed, I was greeted by flower pots upturned all over the place, such a mess in fact that I assumed the garden had been vandalised by some drunken individuals who had over-indulged the Christmas festivities. Then suddenly there was Blackthorn, nonchalantly plodding down the steps towards me."

"How did you catch him? It couldn't have been very easy because you must have been on your own."

"I must admit I did start to panic, but he appeared to be very hungry. He was quite anxious to follow me. I later realised that he must have used a great deal of energy forcing and digging his way out, and that he had left having only partially eaten his Christmas-day treat.

"I was going to ask you, how did he get out of the entrance lobby?"

"He actually dug under the pen. Whereas the actual

enclosures were built like Fort Knox, the entrance lobbies were really only lightweight structures. They were there as a safety precaution in case an otter slipped by whilst I was taking something through into the main pen, fresh bedding perhaps, or for the ease of running a dog otter away into an adjacent pen after he had been with a bitch for mating. That way I could avoid the hassle of catching up an individual and the inevitable stress that's caused. Anyway, somehow he had forced the door open enough at the base for him to squeeze out underneath. He must be mighty strong in the shoulders and neck muscles. Of course, I have always maintained that you otters are no different from badgers, to whom you are closely related."

"How's that then?" Storm enquired inquisitively, falling into my carefully laid trap.

"You can compare badgers to rugger prop-forwards. Both have a low centre of gravity and no neck!"

"Very funny."

"Still," I continued. "Blackthorn was a very, very determined otter. He proceeded to demolish enough of the lobby to escape. That was the easy part. To get out under the original door with two bolts, middle and top still bolted, well I find that very hard to believe."

"But you haven't told me how you actually caught him?"

"That turned out to be quite easy. He was following me everywhere, so I simply opened the basement door into the house and trapped him in the immediate passage. I fetched a travelling crate and in no time he was back inside his pen.

"So if you had locked him in, what was he doing by an upturned boat?" enquired Storm. "Surely you didn't let him out again?"

"I am afraid I did" I started tentatively, "it was entirely my fault again."

"I don't believe this!" exclaimed Storm.

"I am quite sure that I had double checked the bottom bolt," I continued. "In my own mind there was no way I was going to make the same mistake twice, but sure enough two nights later he somehow managed to leave his enclosure again. It was as though he was possessed by some supernatural strength or force. I am still baffled. I had only made temporary repairs to the outer lobby, so this time he was clean away with no difficulty. In the morning there was no sign of him."

"What did you do?" Storm sounded anxious.

"There was not much I could do really I rang the local R.S.P.C.A. centre and advised them that a large, indeed a very large, and rather tame dog otter was now somewhere in the vicinity and that he would tend to come towards you rather than run away. I advised them, if anybody reported seeing him, to try and shut him in somewhere, anywhere, perhaps in a garage or even a garden shed. I repeated the same information to the station sergeant at the local Police Station. He duly filled in the appropriate 'missing persons' form: *lost, one large boy otter!*"

I could see that Storm enjoyed that bit.

"However I did not hold out much hope of finding him," I continued, "and after three days when there had been no response, I had given him up for lost."

"Come on, you must tell me how you eventually found him," Storm was becoming excited again.

"I was in the local grocer's shop and one of the lady assistants who knew about my otters and my work with them suddenly turned to me across the shop, and said quite loudly in front of all the other customers, 'You got your otter back then?' I was dumbfounded. I remember muttering 'no..' and saying how we had not received any news at all. Quickly she began elaborating, 'Oh yes, lots of people have seen him. In fact one night he was seen staring in through the front plate glass doors of the Yacht Club on Knightstone Island; and from inside, someone's Jack Russell terrier had barked at him'."

"Poor Blackthorn, he must have been really scared."

"Well I gather not, because this lady then proceeded to tell me that he had been seen two nights running. In the mornings he was still around because the local fishermen had thrown him a few sprats whilst unloading their catches of cod."

"But I thought Ashleigh was one of those who regularly went fishing from the quay there," Storm continued. "I remember him telling you all about the fish he caught in the different seasons, sprats in November, cod in January and salmon throughout May and June."

"You have a very good memory young lady." I interrupted.

"Ashleigh came with us to the 'Tarka' lecture you presented with me in the very village close to where Tarka was supposed to have been born. Whilst we were waiting, you and he talked for some time about the rivers around there."

"That's right. Weare Giffard is the village, and the Torridge and the Taw are the two rivers. Tarka lived out his tragic life in the

166

'Land of the Two Rivers'. Ashleigh had carried out some lifeboat training out of Appledore, and learnt how to handle the inshore boat over the treacherous bar in the estuary there, practising at the different stages of the incoming and ebbing tides. Well done, you are quite right. But going back to Blackthorn and his situation, Ashleigh had seen him too, but like all the others had assumed that someone else would phone me."

"And they didn't?"

"No, unfortunately they didn't. I knew from the shop assistant that Blackthorn didn't seem in any way scared and, providing no one had deliberately frightened him in the meantime, more than likely he would still be hanging around in the same area."

"So you collected Sharon and went off and caught him, just like that," concluded Storm jumping the gun.

"No, it wasn't quite as easy as that. I did not want to draw attention to the situation by looking for him in broad daylight. With an audience hanging around, I might not have been able to work a situation where I could have caught him cleanly, and that was vital. In any case, I had no idea exactly where he was. I reckoned that it was going to be much better to wait until it was well dark, and for everything to have gone very quiet. Then I hoped he would show himself again. I obviously rang my member of staff Sharon, and she indicated that her husband Kevin would kindly help too. In the meantime I put up a small amount of his favourite food.

"Mackerel?" asked Storm excitedly.

"Yes, he really does love his mackerel, doesn't he, particularly small ones, so that he can enjoy crunching the heads as well."

"Joey's," said Storm brightly, "I like them too."

I took the dish of food to the clubhouse and handed it over to one of the staff. They had heard all about Blackthorn and I explained my plans. They readily agreed to keep the titbits on standby and, if he showed up later that evening, they were going to try and encourage him inside and then trap him in one of the beer cellars."

"And lock him in?"

"Of course."

"Obviously that didn't happen," said Storm, remembering that I had found him by the upturned boat.

"Instead we were very lucky in a different way. I collected Kevin and Sharon as planned. Kevin had rigged up a powerful light which was powered by a car battery. He was going to carry

167

it on his shoulders in a heavy-duty canvas holdall and, when it was switched on, you could see everything and everywhere very clearly. It was perfect. I already had a travelling crate on board the van, so all we needed was lady luck to be with us."

"Blackthorn has been my friend for some while now so presumably everything went to plan."

"Absolutely. Since we had to cover every possible hiding place in such a large area, we decided to simply work our way back through the various old out-buildings that were on the seaward side of the Yacht Club close to the River Severn, so as to avoid him being frightened towards the open sea. We planned to make a move about nine o'clock. By then he might have been keen to start searching for some food. It was absolutely still and quiet and very dark, so we needed to light up all the nooks and crannies. The tide was out in the bay, and I was worried that he might be planning to make his way towards the estuary flats drawn by the gentle lapping of the waves on the far sands.

Drake shelducks were fending off unatached males, would be suitors for their already chosen mates. Over one hundred pairs nest on the Bristol Channel islands of Flat and Steep Holm, but the crowded herring gull colonies are now much reduced due to outbreaks of botulism. Increasingly lazy feeders, the birds have become infected by scavenging the easy pickings of the waste-tips and landfill sites of Bristol. At that moment however, the shelducks contented chattering amongst their extended family flock could have easily triggered Blackthorn's wild instincts.

We had not explored very far, no further really than in and out of the first piles of debris you associate with boats that have been hauled out for repairs, when, there he was, sitting it out in the hollow of a deep coil of rope behind some large wooden crates and drums of spent engine oil. If it had not been for the virtual daylight created by Kevin's light, we could easily have missed him."

"I wonder if he knows we are talking about him now?" interrupted Storm excitedly, "he is only a few yards away from us at this very moment. I presume he is asleep, curled up around Wensum. Perhaps he is dreaming about the time he was out. But you caught him quite easily?" Storm was back with the story.

"Yes Sharon stayed close to Blackthorn. She reassured him that he would soon be safe and kept any direct light off him so as not to frighten him. When I returned from the van with Kevin, we positioned the all important crate so as to incorporate the wall of an adjacent building as one side of our makeshift catching enclosure. The proximity of that building was a bonus because we planned to drive him gently behind even more large containers, and into what would appear to him to be a long dark passage. We moved everything around quietly, and soon he was on his way. Basically the further he went, the narrower the space became, and soon it was the opening to the travelling crate that

Why otters swim under water but close to the surface

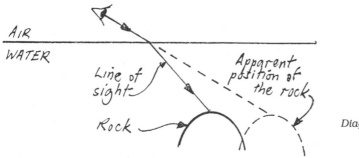

Diagram 2

If you look into the water in a river or pond, the objects in the water or on the river bed or bottom of the pond appear to be displaced from their true position. This is another effect of refraction caused because the refractive index of water is different from the refractive index of air. As shown in Diagram 2, this effect is due to the deviation or refraction of your "line of sight" as you look into the water. See page 181

awaited him. Sharon meanwhile had positioned herself on top the crate ready to drop the trap door into place. The complete operation depended on moving him slowly and eventually towards her. That was plan A anyway!"

"Your idea must have worked."

"Absolutely no problem. In fact I think he was very relieved, when he was safe again in the crate and on his way home with us. I believe his boldness has always been bravado on his part. He went straight into his enclosure with no hesitation. So little fuss in fact, that Willow, his mate next door, never stirred. Within minutes, he had scoffed all his supper too, proving, in fact, that in the meantime he had become very hungry."

"Brilliant" said Storm enthusiastically," and I bet you locked up his door that night like never before."

"And ever since," I added, with a wry smile.

"That fellow Blackthorn been out again?"

Storm jumped in surprise at the interruption. Suddenly Ken was leaning into the enclosure where I was sitting with her. We had been reminiscing about Blackthorn's escape in the new hut that the BBC Natural History Unit had generously donated to the Tamar Otter Sanctuary following their recent filming. Ken was planning to use the hut as a stand-by emergency enclosure for the occasional wild orphaned cub that is brought in to the Trust's care. He and Carwyn had recently strengthened and modified it for that very purpose. Now that otters are recovering quite strongly throughout their original strongholds of Devon and Cornwall, it means that there is now, sadly, the occasional road casualty. If the rescue involves a lactating bitch, then maybe with luck at least one cub is found. If it is also recovered soon enough and is not too dehydrated, then it can often be successfully reared. Another source of stray youngsters occurs when they are three to four months of age and showing the first signs of independence of the nursery holt. Sometimes the holt becomes washed out after sudden heavy rainfall, and they can be the victims of rapidly rising river water and flash-floods. If they are able to swim or are at least strong enough to stay afloat, then again they may be lucky enough to be found. Otherwise sadly they drown. For either reason, at least one individual arrives at North Petherwin every eighteen months or so, although not necessarily at any particular time of the year.

Storm and I were back at North Petherwin on this Saturday in early December preparing to film the following day for a programme called 'Animal Passions'. It was being made by West Country Television and I had promised Storm that I would bring her in early from Somerset, so that I could stay with her for a while, giving her good time to settle before overnighting.

Ken was smiling mischievously, "Your Blackthorn hasn't changed his ways. After I had arrived at the sanctuary the other morning and had unlocked the main shed to start work, I decided to return to the cafe building because I had forgotten to switch on the hot water boiler for the morning drinks. Suddenly I heard one or two very strange noises, so I made my way to where I thought the noise was coming from."

"Was it the wallabies playing?," asked Storm, who had obviously missed Ken's opening remark referring to Blackthorn. "I know when we were filming here with the BBC, they were often to be found sheltering behind the building . Warwick told me he used to take them titbits of cake. I liked Warwick."

"Hang on Storm," I interrupted, "let Ken finish. What did you find?"

"None other than Blackthorn blinking out of the ladies' toilet!"

"What was he doing in there?" asked Storm incredulously,

"Looking for a bitch I guess," said Ken with a twinkle in his eye.

I smiled, as Storm obviously missed the point of Ken's mischievous remark.

Ken continued. "I quickly persuaded Blackthorn to follow me back into the lavatory. I locked him in there until Carwyn arrived, and we could organise a crate. Then I immediately set off to check the other otters."

"Were they all still in their enclosures?" enquired Storm.

"Oh yes, but I sensed there had been an awful lot of overnight activity. I reckoned that a wild bitch had come up the Boleswater Brook on our lower boundary and had somehow found her way through the marsh into the sanctuary."

"Do you think Blackthorn went out to meet her?" I enquired.

"He's done it before, I know he has." Storm was beside herself with excitement, and both Ken and I looked at her in disbelief.

"How can you be sure of that?" I asked.

"Well, you remember the first night I was here after the BBC filming started. I told you there was one helluva rumpus going on. That was it, it was Blackthorn going out, I bet it was. There was bickering everywhere. It was Ripple and Pebble getting very jealous, and Wensum too. I can see it all clearly now. Whoever the wild bitch was, she didn't leave till well after dawn, because it wasn't that long before I heard Ken unlocking the main shed where I was over-nighting."

"That explains a lot," Ken added. "I soon realised that more than likely he had done it several times before. I discovered his route out of the enclosure; there were heavy boulders pushed aside, and where the wire mesh was weakened, it had been lifted. All of this at the very point where the water overflows his pool and tumbles away into the duck pond."

"I was just telling Storm how strong he is and how he can shift almost anything with his strong shoulder and neck muscles," I added.

"Although Blackthorn had made quite an opening for himself, I think Wensum still stayed inside." Ken continued. "No way would she have wanted to confront a young wild bitch seeking a new territory, and that's what this newcomer was. I have known for some time there have been otters out on the main river, so if they have successfully bred there are going to be young adults seeking new mates."

"Have you heard one whistling recently?" I asked.

"We are not here late enough on a regular basis, David," Ken added. "But now Storm has confirmed my suspicions, I think Carwyn might stay on at night to see if he can gather some information."

"Do you know, it makes me wonder whether that's just what Blackthorn was doing when he went out in Somerset. There is no doubt that he was absolutely determined to go, and in the stillness of cold and frosty December nights, he may well have been hearing the plaintive calls of a bitch. The whistling could have easily carried across the estuary to where our family group was living. Come to think of it, I am reminded of three independent records of wild otters close to us over the years.

A local self-employed window cleaner, a fellow approaching retirement, told me he knew where otters were. Always sceptical of such remarks at first, I listened with great interest as he recalled frequently walking the lower reaches of the River Axe. He would stop regularly where the exit of the fresh water from the nearby Levels into the tidal channel was controlled by sluice gates. At that place he had, from time to time, heard the high-pitched whistle of an otter 'calling' for a mate.

An ex water-bailiff at Blagdon Lake, one of a complex of waters belonging to the Bristol Waterworks Company in north Somerset, could remember otters loitering with intent around the trout hatchery. The lake's overspill waters feed into the Yeo River, which finally, and many miles later flows through tidal saltings to the estuary. It is the well recognised story of the way an otter moves from its summer haunts and holts to its lonely winter sojourn close to the seashore."

"And is Williamson's classic tale of *Tarka* in a nutshell too," commented Ken.

"I know, and before I leave this area altogether, I can also remember a machine driver collecting eels for me to feed my collection whilst drainage works involved straightening a cut adjacent to where the M5 was being constructed south across the area. Not only did he collect bucketfuls as they spilt from the dredged mud onto the bank, but by the time I came from Bristol

172

to collect them the following morning, there were otter footprints, or seals as we sometimes call them, all over the soft ground close to the swing bucket."

"Were the wild otters able to find any at all?" Storm seemed worried.

"Yes. The driver only left his cab to collect the longer and more visible ones. I am sure there were plenty left for the pair of otters, that I believe were living briefly together, to collect under the cover of darkness."

"Where was the third occasion?" interrupted Storm eagerly.

"Some years ago now in January time there was a dreadful storm in the Bristol Channel, coinciding with one of the highest of the spring tides," I began. "It seemed as if the very eye of the storm was centred directly over our part of the Severn estuary, Brean Down and the islands of Flat and Steep Holm. The severe gale-force winds changed direction entirely in about two hours. Originally they were from the south-east as the weather deteriorated, but at the height of the storm, they were coming at us from the north-west. There was considerable damage to the seaside promenades of Weston-super-Mare and Burnham-on-Sea, and dozens of properties were badly flooded. Everywhere the high incoming tide had encountered the barrier of the swollen fresh floodwater of the river Severn and so had breached the sea and river defences and nowhere worse than along the River Parrett. There was a terrible loss of livestock as many hundreds of sheep were drowned by the invading sea. The nearby low-lying areas, the Levels, were a disaster area. Now when the next evening's high tide was due at about five or six o'clock, a person whom I was to meet later, decided to see if there was going to be a repetition of the events at high water. He approached the seafront in Weston-super-Mare close to where it was most likely to be flooded again. He parked his car at the back of the local Technical College and was therefore only a short walk away from any forthcoming action. In fact he wasn't a stone's throw from where we had recaptured Blackthorn. As he left his car, a large animal suddenly appeared out of one of the nearby gardens and dashed out of sight under other parked cars. He saw it only briefly, but nevertheless quite clearly. Later that evening in a local hotel he was telling a certain Ross Kennedy, whose company supplied the meat for our otters, about the animal he had seen. Ross said to come and see me and our otters to confirm, or otherwise, what he thought he had seen."

"And did he? Or is this going to be another of your long stories Dad?" Storm interrupted impatiently, eager as ever to hear the outcome of a story as quickly as possible."

"Oh yes, the following morning he called without warning, and minutes after hearing his recollections, I was showing him Rowan who was curled up in her holt. He described the animal he had seen as being almost creamy in colour, and the coat as having quite a silky texture. Rowan had obviously dried out overnight, and still asleep upside down was displaying the gentle and delicate tones of her underfur for all and sundry to see."

"Her coat was all the colours of a wild mushroom, even having a hint of pink in the softest hair," said Storm with just a hint of sarcasm, "I know what you are going to say next from the talks you give."

I carried on ignoring Storm's wickedness. She did not know either that I had already written those lines earlier in the text of 'Stormforce'!

"It was just like that, almost identical, same colour," the fellow was almost shouting in joy as he was quickly realising what he had seen. "But it was much longer," he finally exclaimed, gesticulating with outstretched arms.

"So I showed him Tigger after we had quietly crept in on him. I woke Tigger gently, and you know Tigger, he was immediately curious and came over to say hello."

'That's much more like the size. He was every bit as big as this fella and all dried out too. What do you say this one's name is again?'

"Tigger," I replied, "he's a five year old dog otter, he was bred here and...."

'Fantastic, great, lovely creatures....'

"With that he was gone, as quickly as he had arrived, very eager I guess to confirm to his friends exactly what he had seen a couple of nights previously."

"Sounds to me as if the otter he saw was going to become like the fish that got away," added Ken drily, gesturing with his arms simultaneously.

"What was that about him getting away?" enquired Storm.

Now was not the time to explain I thought, and so carried on.

"The fellow hadn't stayed long enough for me to explain that the dog otter he had luckily spotted had been washed up, or even literally thrown ashore, by the force of the tide and gale in the Severn estuary. He had lain up exhausted all the previous night and through the following day."

"One mighty relieved otter I guess," remarked Storm. "When the fellow saw him out in the road, presumably he had just woken up."

"Yes, and I wanted to explain to him too, that you otters, when ashore and out of the water for a long time and therefore very dry, resemble common seals in colour after they have been hauled out for hours on their favourite sandbank at low water. They lie there dozing, heads and flippers arched aloft almost quarter-moon in shape and with all the appearance of Viking longships with upturned prows and sterns. Late one autumn afternoon with Helen, I watched common seals on the sands of Loch Gruinart on the island of Islay. The seals were almost honey in colour, having stayed to take advantage of the sunshine for as long as possible before allowing themselves grudgingly to be floated off on the tide. They were enchanting. Mind you, at the same time we were also listening to the rafts of drake eider ducks chattering amongst themselves. We were wondering too, for the icing on the cake, whether we might just possibly glimpse an otter foraging along the distant shore."

"Or even just hear one," interrupted Ken.

"Imagine the same place," I continued, "against the backdrop of the Paps of Jura dusted in winter snow, with thousands of barnacle and Greenland white-fronted geese in from their Arctic breeding grounds. Then it must be one of the top ten wildlife areas in the whole of western Europe.

"When you have stopped enthusing about Gruinart or wherever, please will you tell me some other stories about otters escaping?" enquired Storm. "Ken, what about the otters you looked after in Norfolk? Surely some of those were as naughty as Blackthorn?"

"I will come back and tell you a tale or two about them before I leave later this afternoon, but for the moment I must hurry on to feed everybody. The weather is turning for the worse, and the forecast is for more overnight rain with the temperatures dropping as well."

"It doesn't bode well for filming in the morning," I added. "Storm, I will now go and prepare your food and bedding. Then we will talk a little longer before I must leave too."

"See you here in about an hour," said Ken. As he turned to go, he tightened the hood of his heavy waterproof jacket, as the wind threw the rain against the windows of the hut.

EIGHT

"YOU DO TAKE MY LIFE WHEN YOU DO TAKE
THE MEANS WHEREBY I LIVE"

"You never told me that I was a having new enclosure," said Storm excitedly. "I was wondering why Carwyn had been around so much lately."

"I have been taking stock of a rapidly changing situation," I replied. "Following the setback in my health earlier last year, I have known for a while now that I would have to reappraise my contribution to otter conservation."

"I thought our book *Stormforce* was the project to describe some of your work with otters over the years," interrupted Storm.

"Yes that's right, and writing it has been very much part of my plans, especially describing the past seven years with you. I've really appreciated having you close at hand and being involved in all that I have achieved."

"So why couldn't we have continued doing that where we were?" insisted Storm.

"As you know, my plans originally were to continue keeping several otters. I was intending for instance, to carry on with my successful breeding programme."

"Is that why you were holding Ripple and Pebble back?"

"Yes, I wanted to run another dog with them, a youngster in the Cider, Blackthorn mould."

"Gentle giants you mean," said Storm, remembering my oft quoted and affectionate comment about two of my most influential dog otters."

"That's absolutely right, a dog which would both sire well, but which would, at the same time, be a laid-back individual capable of fitting in with anybody, anywhere and with any situation. We mustn't forget the number of cubs I have been able to pass on to Philip and Jeanne Wayre at the Otter Trust at Bungay in Suffolk. Those individuals have significantly strengthened both their

177

breeding and release programmes."

"What's changed then?" Storm pursued her enquiries.

"Throughout the last few years the otters which have been set free have bred so well that English Nature can now safely reduce the re-introduction programme. Many reports have now been received of youngsters becoming established close to their original release sites. That information has come not only from committed volunteers keeping a watchful eye on the various individuals' behaviour patterns, but also from records and sightings from the field officers of different official bodies."

"Like the various Water Authorities and the Environment Agency," responded Storm cleverly.

"You're very knowledgeable and up-to-date tonight," I joked. "The National Rivers Authority also has many staff in the field and many amateur enthusiasts are monitoring how the offspring, born to the original dogs and bitches, have moved on and further away to yet new territories. English Nature set down the important criteria at the inception of the release programme in the early 80s, and now nearly twenty years later, a most successful scheme can be greatly scaled down. It's good news, isn't it?"

"So no more breeding by you ever again?" Storm sounded disconsolate.

"English Nature will only be looking for cubs for topping-up purposes," I guess.

"How do you mean, how do you 'top-up' with otter cubs?"

"I am sorry, I am misleading you," I added, " There will always be a few cubs available but only bred by the Otter Trust, and these will be held on standby. Say, for example, it is obvious from the volunteers' observations that an adult breeding dog has gone missing off his territory....."

"He will have probably been killed on the road," interrupted Storm impatiently.

"Yes, could be, but not necessarily so; Jarvis's mother was a road casualty, but there are other causes. Occasionally otters can drown in fyke nets. These are set submerged in rivers for catching eels as they make their run downstream to the open sea; poachers can also set illegal nets for salmon, and otters, ever inquisitive, can be fatally trapped and sadly can drown ."

"How can people do that?" Storm's irritation and anger were rising, reflecting, not for the first occasion, her concern about the cruelty that human beings impose on her fellow creatures. I continued, anxious not to allow Storm to become upset again.

"Well, whatever the cause, if there is a sad loss, then another individual, captive bred, can be slotted into the original's place or territory. So we would be 'topping-up' the family group again."

"I see, but no more trios back to the wild?"

"Well, maybe here and there, but otters are now slowly increasing in numbers and are spreading out in two directions in this country. Firstly, there are the offspring from the original release sites where, following the problems of pollution, habitat loss and so on in the 50s and 60s, collection-bred otters could be placed relatively easily. Quite simply there were no wild otters at all surviving with established territories on many water courses in eastern and southern England. Secondly, from the strongholds that remained mainly in the Westcountry and Wales, there is evidence of young adults now dispersing to repopulate old traditionally inhabited areas. Indeed in some parts, particularly in Cambridgeshire and Lincolnshire, and to the south around the tributaries of the Thames the two groups are now merging of their own accord. English Nature think it right that the expansion should continue in this natural way."

"How many cubs have the Otter Trust released?"

"Over a hundred now. The Trust's projects and release sites have all been carefully cleared and closely monitored by the government scientists; people such as Dr Don Jefferies, who was senior scientist at the then Nature Conservancy Council, now known as English Nature. More general research on otters was carried out by other researchers. These were all the M's, Messrs Mitchell-Jones, MacDonald and Mason, and Elizabeth Lenton and Jane Twelves too. Then there was the input over the years by the various conservation officers of the Otter Trust, and of course not forgetting that from Philip and Jeanne Wayre themselves."

"You don't hear an awful lot about all the work they have accomplished, do you?"

"They certainly don't shout about it from the rooftops ,although they have every justification. You see Storm, there are some in the conservation field, as in all walks of life, who are no more than publicity seekers. Often you will find their input is in direct contrast to the recognition they receive in the media, particularly from television. But it is, without question, no mean achievement for the Otter Trust to breed not only the cubs for release, but also the replacement otters as well, in order to keep the reintroduction programme on course. Before 1970, when the first cubbings occurred, the British otter had not been previously bred in any collection since 1881. That last occasion was in the London Zoo, and no one is sure either that the female concerned was not already pregnant when she arrived.

"When did your successes start?"

"In the very early 80s, and then increasingly so in the years following".

"And how long do otters live in the Otter Trust collections and with you?"

"Obviously not all otters live to ten years plus. There are the unlucky individuals who fall foul of life's problems. Some will develop cancerous growths. There are those who suffer from kidney stones, which prove initially very painful and ultimately, fatal. Abcesses forming around rotten teeth from middle age onwards are a nuisance too. Finally, individuals pick up viruses, particularly Leptospirosis which is passed on by rats, with which they cannot cope, even with the help of the veterinary surgeons and their drugs, the anti-biotics and so on."

"I've heard Olivia calling them anti-buy-buckets, when she is helping you," remarked Storm happily.

"However, Storm, to breed and to have available for release over one hundred unrelated individuals, and to retain more stock to cover unexpected and sad losses is a great achievement. Few people writing or broadcasting about the recovery of the otter have seen fit to recognise the role of the Trust's remarkable efforts."

"Will you speak about it in *Stormforce* ?"

"Well, we are commenting on the success right now, aren't we? When I have read you the completed text which, hopefully, will be ready shortly, you will see that I do refer to it from time to time in our overall story."

"Why haven't people made more of it?"

"Storm, that is a long story. I have hinted at one reason, 'professional jealousy'. There was a letter of late in the monthly BBC Wildlife magazine, which is circulated in the UK and also has a worldwide readership; it is very well respected for its content. The content of the letter indicated that the Norfolk Wildlife Trust had conducted a survey of otters on Norfolk rivers for the Environment Agency. Over 30% of the sites surveyed had active signs of otters, a good increase on the figures shown by the 1994 National Survey, and well up from the mid 80s when only tiny fragments of the existing otter populations remained in the county. The Norfolk Wildlife Trust clearly indicated that the increase in otters not only in Norfolk, but for East Anglia as a whole, has largely been attributable to the very reintroduction programme, that we have been talking about. They concluded that the released cubs and their offspring, which are in turn breeding so well, have probably saved the otter from extinction in Norfolk"

"So there we are then" exclaimed Storm, "all down in black and white for everyone to see. Great news".

"Much more important are my plans for the future, and I am sure you are going to be excited by those," I added. "However it's late now, shall we continue tomorrow evening?"

With that, we parted company for the night, and I left Storm exploring her new home.

Why otters swim under water but close to the surface

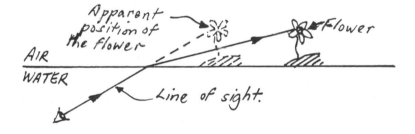

Diagram 3

If you could put your head under water and look at objects that are in the air above the water, your "line of sight" would again be refracted. The position of the objects above the water would appear to be displaced. This effect is shown in Diagram 3. See page 192

"I had come down from university and I had exactly two years to create and construct my wildlife park in Bristol, before it was to be opened to the general public by the late Sir Peter Scott. I was going to specialise in breeding only British animals and birds, and I planned to display them in and around a beautiful little valley. There was mature woodland, overgrown paddocks and old buildings, all waiting to be adapted. An added bonus was a beautiful tumbling stream. The river Trym was then still the haunt of Kingfishers, although the eleven acres were not five miles from the centre of the urban sprawls of the city of Bristol.

"What had your park to do with your future conservation work for otters?" asked Storm as we sat together. I was planning to explain to her how the emphasis of my work now might not have to change that significantly from what I was doing all those years ago.

"I started work in my park in June '65, and by mid June '67, the first visitors were flocking in."

"But surely everything has altered a great deal in the thirty years since then?," Storm continued.

"That's what is so surprising," I replied, "it hasn't really changed at all. Part of my approach to wildlife conservation then was quite new. It has also stood the test of time since, and I don't think there is any great need to change now. The years may have rolled by but the necessary elements required for a successful conservation programme and message remain the same today."

"I'm intrigued." Storm was clearly prepared to hear me out.

"The wildlife park was in direct competition for visitors with Bristol Zoo which, although managed on traditional lines, was well established and was then, under the stewardship of the the head curator Don Packham, probably the best provincial collection in the country. But, at the same time, the second of the new breed of large safari parks was also being created at Longleat House, near Bath. It was therefore almost on our doorstep too. Launched by the flamboyant Lord Bath within the grounds of his estate, there was a partnership with the Chipperfield family who were of long standing in the circus world."

"Don't talk to me about circuses and all that they represent!" Storm was adamant, "I would much prefer to hear how you managed to survive the competition. It couldn't have been easy with the public being attracted as usual by the most spectacular animals. I suppose they saw elephants and polar bears and the like in the Zoo, and lions, giraffe and monkeys roaming at large in the safari park."

"Exactly, and at Longleat, it only needed one of the monkeys to play some practical joke on the visitors, as they sat in their car or coach, and there were headline news in both the national and local newspapers, as well as on regional television, for the following few days."

"In time to encourage the next weekend's visitors." interrupted Storm.

"You are absolutely right. You could rely on a monkey pulling a car radio aerial to bits. or reaching into a vehicle and stealing something valuable from inside. although all the windows were supposed to be kept shut. The publicity boys had a field day!"

"You were saying about your park" murmured Storm, as I drifted from my original storyline.

"It was never my intention to simply display a collection of native animals and birds. Some of them were coming under threat. and I did not realise that for some, otters for example, the situation was already serious. So I was aware that as well as showing our native creatures, and importantly trying to breed some of them, it was vital as well to make others aware of the very serious factors affecting their future survival."

"Are you telling me that by the time you were opening the park, you did not realise that my ancestors were already deep in trouble?" Storm seemed disappointed in me. and rightly so. I pressed on.

"I had read Rachel Carson's *Silent Spring*, which although based on American evidence. was to act as a watershed in the world of wildlife conservation politics. I had realised that youngsters, say between seven and twelve, were the most likely age group to be receptive to the information. If they could take some of the facts on board, and although the examination years of their teens and twenties would take them away from conservation issues, there was a good chance they would return to making the protection of our wildlife one of the priorities in their lives as parents. A strong impact on them needed to be achieved initially."

"They also needed to learn to care for the places where that wildlife lives, its habitat," interrupted Storm sternly.

"Yes, you are absolutely right again. These areas are vital too, if not more so in fact".

"Is that why you are still lecturing today?" asked Storm.

"My lecturing career began from giving conducted tours in my wildlife park. Youngsters were obviously going on organised school visits to other collections. However, I specialised in giving guided tours to my parties. Subsequently the children and their teachers felt the visits were a more factual experience, complemented as they were by information sheets and questionnaires to be completed.

In the months of the spring and summer terms, whenever the weather was kind, the staff, whom I trained, and myself could find ourselves conducting up to five or six tours daily. On such days there could have been as many as two or three hundred youngsters visiting. The children became more involved, the talks were personal and therefore their visits became far more memorable for them. The tours became very heavily requested and proved to be the basis of a very popular wildlife park.

The children would see me handle the hawks and owls; in springtime we would perhaps be bottle-feeding fox and badger cubs ; in the summer there were deer fawns to be hand-reared as well. But always the highlight of the tour was the hand-feeding of the seals. It wasn't long before I was receiving invitations to visit schools."

"With live exhibits?"

"Of course."

"I bet you didn't take a seal to school."

"I used to take them to television studios for programmes such as 'Animal Magic', but that's another story altogether."

"Maybe we could put all those stories into another book?," Storm exclaimed excitedly.

"That's a good idea for the future," but I did not get side-tracked and continued. "Anyway, I always felt it was equally important for parents to see the same exhibits and to hear the same information as their children, in order to secure a more lasting impact for each family, and therefore I would offer to stay and complete evening presentations. By the way, Helen and I first met when I visited her school with some young badger cubs."

"How many years ago was that?" I could sense that Storm was intrigued.

"Too long ago to try and remember but a frightening figure, if I worked it out exactly," I replied smiling. "Suffice to say, I was already lecturing regularly in schools around Bristol over thirty years ago!"

"So was that when you first started talking about all the problems we otters face?"

"Absolutely, and ever since. My presentations have been the perfect opportunity to draw attention to the worrying concerns we have about your relations. Even today you know how much time I spend on the problems, with the overall content of the talks always much more than just straight facts about otters. In the early days there was a quotation that I had printed on all my literature. It is attributable to the late King George VI, at the time of the creation of the first of our National Parks. The words were relevant then and still are now. He said: *The wildlife of today is not ours to dispose of as we please; we have it in trust, we must account for it to those who come after.* It's good, isn't it? I kept it for years, although for the youngsters' literature I needed something brief. So I came up with: *Conservation through Education.*"

"That really sums up your work. But you use a different saying now," added Storm immediately. "Is that simply because these days you concentrate on otters?"

"*For all, but more particularly children, who also seek understanding between humans and other animals*, attributable to the late Gavin Maxwell," I added. "Yes, because his name is synonymous with otters, and I have always respected his emphasis on *particularly children*. Of course he wrote *Ring of Bright Water*, a book which was not only a best seller in the United Kingdom, but worldwide too".

"Do you think *Stormforce* will sell as well as *Ring of Bright Water*?" Storm interrupted.

"If only," I sighed, "but at least, as with Maxwell's book, *Stormforce* is a true story about real otters, written by a person, whom I guess, has spent even longer than Maxwell did in their close company," I added.

"*Ring of Bright Water* is a lovely title though, it's very...." Storm was struggling for the right words.

"Evocative," I suggested, "captures a feeling of wildness and mystery, doesn't it? Do you know what the words refer to?"

I looked at Storm but nothing was forthcoming; suddenly she was lost in some distant world.

"You are going to tell me anyway aren't you?," she demanded moments later.

"Your coat is dense and waterproof. It consists of two layers, a short velvety undercoat and a top coat of long stiff guard hairs."

"Very similar to Sasha's."

"When you are on land, air is trapped between these two layers and acts as an insulation. When you dive some of the air is forced out creating a chain of bubbles which rise to the surface, indicating of course, where you are swimming underwater. Hence...."

"A ring of bright water," added Storm quickly.

"The masters of otter-hounds had long recognised the subtle

185

differences between the bubbles left by an otter's trail as he or she entered the water, and the natural bubbles of the river water created by the ebb and flow of the current; and before you say anything, I know you don't want to discuss otter hunting and those who found pleasure in taking part," I added quickly.

"Was *Tarka the Otter* not a true story then?" enquired Storm immediately. "Surely that must rank as one of *the* otter books."

"I will tell you something about Henry Williamson, who was the author of *Tarka* in a moment or two, but before we leave titles, I think Philip Wayre's *The River People* reflects the personalities of otters. It's brief and much to the point."

"I like *On the Swirl of the Tide* too," enthused Storm, "written by the MaCaskills. At least the passages you have read to me. Wasn't it based on their observations over ten years on a Scottish sea loch? I became very attached to Bodach; he so reminded me of Tigger, all muscle and very butch. However, *Stormforce* conjures up the idea of a story that's equally dramatic. Anyway I think so."

I smiled at Storm's undoubted bias.

"Williamson did have a wild otter cub for a while. Its mother had been shot by a farmer who was on a rabbiting expedition. Williamson helped to retrieve two cubs from the holt but only one was alive. He persuaded his cat to suckle it. Luckily she had a single kitten at the time."

"You have always said that an otter needs luck," said Storm, "like me."

"Yes, but sadly unlike with you, this one's good fortune ran out. Whilst Williamson was rearing it as his companion, he would walk it regularly along the banks of streams and rivers. But one day, tragedy struck. Williamson found it caught in a gin trap."

"The poor creature," gasped Storm. "How terrible! You see, I have told you time and again, that it is people who have caused so much pain to animals over the years."

I could see that Storm had been visibly upset; I felt sure she could sense the agony and fear that Williamson's beloved cub must have experienced as it lay trapped. She was clearly sharing the pain of a fellow wild animal, but in this case that of another otter. In order not to distress Storm further, I had no intention of describing in any more detail than necessary how Williamson, having managed to release his cub in order to carry it home, agonisingly allowed it to slip from his grasp. It disappeared never to return. I wanted to spare Storm from the truth, that

Williamson knew that three toes had almost been severed in the trap and that, although he searched for weeks both close to his home and also farther afield, as far in fact as the estuary downstream, he was never to see his cub again. There was no trace in all the footprints of the many wild otters he subsequently examined of an otter with a deformed foot. But it was from this tracking of wild otters, and how they survived, or not, the hunting by hounds aided by followers, that the story of *Tarka* began to evolve.

Storm was still visibly upset in the half light of her new den, as I attempted to fudge the facts. Secretly I was cursing that the true story behind Tarka had arisen in this way.

"But Williamson managed to release his cub successfully," I said determinedly. "Obviously it was in some pain, and that is sadly why it broke free and ran away."

"And never came back?"

"No, it didn't, although it had been accustomed to responding to Williamson's call. But Williamson did spend a long time looking for it, and in fact on his travels he came across the many people, who regularly used the main river and its banks to gain their livelihood. Among them were the various fishermen, both those who worked the river's freshwaters, and also those whose living was won from the tidal reaches closer to the open sea."

But regrettably, in my determination to keep the truth from Storm, I committed a self-imposed gaffe.

"And he would regularly join the hunt followers," I continued.

"I thought you were going to leave off about people, who used to go chasing us with packs of dogs, believing it to be fun." Storm was in sarcastic yet defiant mood again.

"Although, sadly, he himself never managed to be in a position to either call or see his otter again, at least by associating with the hunt followers he acquired many reports of a rather tame individual repeatedly being seen."

"So perhaps good fortune did eventually come back into its life," persisted Storm.

"I am sure it did," I added hastily. I was relieved; I felt the distress of the moments previously was passing and I continued in an up-beat mood, attempting to return to our original conversation.

"Isn't it obvious to you," I said, "that all the best stories written, or indeed the best work carried out on behalf of otters, have been achieved by individuals, who have experienced a never to be forgotten moment with, or sighting of, a wild otter? Maxwell had his own otters and lived amongst wild otters, and I have just told you about Henry Williamson. Now I must briefly tell you something about those who have researched into otters and the problems they face."

Storm, as impatient as ever, indeed as Olivia is when she becomes slightly lost within a conversation, interrupted me immediately.

"How do you *research* an otter?"

"Whenever an individual, a scientist for example, sets out to resolve a difficulty by collecting all the known facts, we say, 'oh so and so is carrying out research, or researching into, whatever....' With such notoriously difficult animals to observe as wild otters, and remember to what lengths your mother went to avoid being seen, then finally the input from the volunteer watchers, however insignificant their observations may seem initially, can suddenly make a most vital contribution."

"So who have been these scientists?" asked Storm," eager as ever to hear the rest of the story."

"Having taken on board and sifted the mass of information, the researchers conclude their work by writing up their studies," I continued. "Then statutory bodies, English Nature for instance, and latterly the Environment Agency put forward their recommendations as to how things should change in practice."

"You still haven't told me exactly who has contributed most to our recovery." Storm's patience was becoming stretched .

"They are all scientists that we mentioned, when talking about the Otter Trust's release programme. There was Dr Paul Chanin, who is presently at the Department of Continuing Adult Education at Exeter University. He published a preliminary paper in 1978, and subsequently followed that with his very important book in 1985, 'The Natural History of Otters'. With Don Jefferies, he was really responsible for revealing how certain agricultural chemicals, introduced in the mid 50s, were accumulating in particular animals and birds at the head of food chains."

"Explain, please," said Storm resolutely again, "explain a food chain."

"Many of the chemicals were used on arable crops, wheat, maize and so on. We live in a wet and windy climate; some of the sprays were washed into the soil, and into ditches, or were blown onto or into hedgerows and the vegetation that grows rank around the edge of fields. Other animals and birds, whilst feeding, absorb the chemicals into their systems; a residue builds up and accumulates. The sparrowhawk preys on small birds by skimming over their targets, Chaffinches, linnets and the like, and plucking them off the top of the hedgerows with the roll of a Lightning fighter." I could see Storm enjoyed that bit, but I quickly returned to the explanation.

"The accumulation of the residue of the sprays is most evident in the hunter that is at the head of a particular food chain. Sparrowhawks, as well as many other birds of prey, and perhaps most famously the peregrine falcon, were soon laying eggs that were infertile. There was an immediate and catastrophic decline in their numbers."

"I can work it out," interrupted Storm excitedly, "sprays were also washed into the wetland vegetation and streams. Small creatures take in the spray, I mean the chemicals, and they are eaten by fish."

"Herons eat fish," I interrupted.

"And otters eat fish too, I can see it all now. Do you mean otters weren't able to have cubs?"

"That's right, and of course one of the favourite foods of otters is ....."

"Eels!" Storm exclaimed. "Mum was always looking for eels in the wet grass." Storm had the answers ready.

"Eels showed then, and can still reveal today, some of the greatest concentrations of residues in their fatty tissues of any prey species." I added.

"So herons and those divers you were talking about, they must have been affected badly as well."

"Yes they were. But sadly Storm, when the scientists had warned the powers that be that the otter was virtually disappearing, and although the Government initially banned the use of many chemicals, one insecticide, Dieldrin, was still permitted to be used in industry. It's unbelievable how short sighted they were."

"I thought the American lady was warning us."

"She was, and our scientists indeed confirmed their own worst fears, but the Government only half shut the door with the evidence pointing otherwise. Don Jefferies' and Paul Chanin's work set the standard by which others could then conduct more detailed studies on particular issues facing otters. However, they were, without doubt, two of the scientists who first came to grips with the quite catastrophic declines that had set in from the mid-fifties onwards. Indeed Paul is even now still much to the fore in vital research work, which will hopefully lead to otters further recovering their numbers. He has recruited volunteers....."

"Like those who previously helped English Nature..." interrupted Storm.

"to collect the spraints or droppings. Each otter's dung contains individual DNA, which makes it possible to identify and sex the animals and thus obviously track where they go. So there will be important clues about the various factors which affect the population of otters."

"Where are they doing this?," inquired Storm.

"The scientists have chosen Devon because the population is already showing a marked recovery there. The project is based on a partnership between the Environment Agency, the Government's Conservation Agency and the Universities of Exeter and Aberdeen. It's in the Aberdeen laboratories where the DNA is separated. The other groups are from the three Wildlife Trusts in Devon, Somerset and Hampshire. By this method, they have already been able to follow some of the individuals for over a year."

"It really does give you hope for the future, doesn't it?"

"It was described in a major national newspaper as being 'the dawn of a new era for conservation, particularly for studying nocturnal animals.' But we must not forget the many other problems which are still occurring all too frequently. In another article in the very same newspaper, there was a description of how on the border of Wiltshire and south Gloustershire, the river life of the Sherston Avon and Luckington Brook, including thousands of crayfish, was killed by an insecticide used in spraying and in sheep-dips. The crayfish species is the white-clawed, our only native freshwater species and nationally protected. The Environment Agency said that, tragically, at least half of the population was wiped out by the incident. So it's not all good news yet."

"What about that fellow with the strange name I heard the BBC people talking about, when we were filming with them last autumn?" Storm's mind was racing ahead of mine.

"You mean Dr Hans Kruuk? He has an international reputation for his studies on animal behaviour. I can remember watching many years ago his programme about wild dogs in East Africa; it was filmed in one of the National Parks, Serengeti or Ngorogoro Crater, somewhere like that. The story was told around Solo, an individual who had become isolated as an outcast even from his own family group or pack."

"An outcast, what's that?" Storm was in difficulty again.

Keep it short, I thought to myself, or I really will be here all night!

"A wild dog pack may have up to 20 members. They hunt, feed and live out their family lives together, including giving birth to their young. In fact everything, defending their territory, searching for food and even overcoming their common problems, is carried out within the structure of a social group, with a clear definition of duties for various individuals. The large apes, and many of the species of monkeys are good examples, and some animals and birds gather in colonies for the breeding season. For example, the fur seals congregate in vast numbers on the frozen shores of Antarctica or on the windswept Falkland Islands."

"Penguins have their family colonies, tens of thousands of pairs too" commented Storm, "Emperor, adélie, macaroni, rockhopper, gentoo, jackass, and their name fits, doesn't it, braying as they do like donkeys." Storm was keen to show off her knowledge of names, however I was not so sure that all of those that Storm listed actually lived in that particular area of the southern oceans! From memory and before needing further reference I could recall chinstrap and adélie for Deception and Paullet islands respectively and macaroni and king for South Georgia.

I hurried on. "Yes that's right," I agreed hastily, "Wild dogs are so different from otters, whom as you know live quite individual lives, particularly the bitches. Short-clawed otters who inhabit some of the great river systems of the Far East, remote areas of the Mekong Delta for example, are possibly the one exception."

"How does Solo fit into all this?"

"When you live that closely together nearly all of the time, well..... try and imagine it, you are never really out of sight or sound of each other....."

"....or smell either," Storm interrupted as she began to think of her world.

"....or of parents, grandparents, aunts and uncles, and don't you dare say cousins, nephews and nieces." I added quickly and jokingly to forestall yet another interruption from Storm.

"At least in my world," I added, "we can shut doors or go into different rooms."

"....or visit a friend. I was falling out with my brothers and *we*

191

were only together for six weeks".

"So Solo fell foul of his family and became an outcast from them, but in the film was seen to be trailing his family group, ever hoping that he would be re-admitted, and become friends with them again. It was a sad and harrowing story."

Storm was suddenly quiet. For a few moments I was sure the memories of the short time spent with her mother and brothers had come flooding back. I have never been althogether sure whether they were happy or sad times. Again I wondered whether she might be imagining what life would have meant for her in spring and summer in the hills high on Exmoor, or in autumn and winter in the muddy creeks of the estuaries of the Bristol Channel and the Severn Sea . Nevertheless fate had been kind to her. If she had not been spotted by Graham Burrows, and then so carefully nursed by his wife Francesca in those first few critical hours, she clearly would not have survived. Her almost ambassadorial role and the influence she can now exert by her very presence on young people's thoughts for the future well-being of all the precious living species on planet earth would have

Why otters swim under water but close to the surface

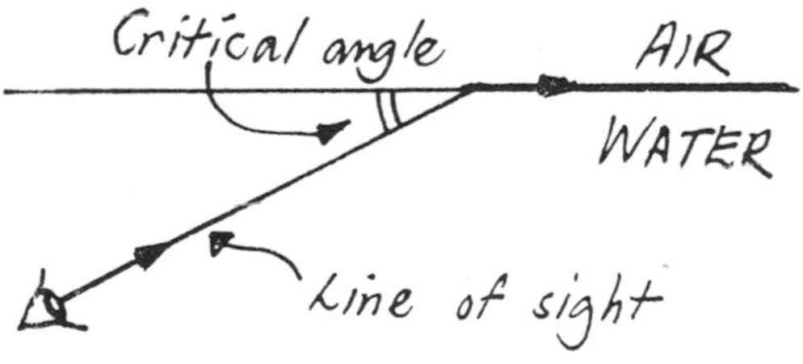

Diagram 4

Now a strange thing happens if you look out from under the water and change the angle between your "line of sight" and the surface of the water. As you make that angle smaller, you would reach a "critical angle" at which your "line of sight" would be bent or refracted so that it would lie along the surface of the water. If you make this angle smaller than the "critical angle", instead of seeing the objects above the water, the surface of the water acts as a mirror; when you look at the surface of the water, you will see the reflection of the objects which are under the water and on the river bed or bottom of the pond. These effects are shown in Diagrams 4 and 5. See page 196 for Diagram 5.

never been realised. The imponderables are never ending.

I jolted both myself and Storm out of our lost thoughts by suddenly hastening on. I was determined not to become side-tracked again.

"Hans Kruuk came home to the United Kingdom after his East African experience to begin a new period of research into the social behaviour of badgers," I began. He was based at the Terrestrial Research Unit at Banchory, near Aberdeen in Scotland, where Helen and I met him for the first time over twenty years ago. We gave him our family of badgers to study."

"That's another story for the next book," Storm interrupted,

"Having concluded that project, he continued his studies in Scotland with otters keeping a few individuals for close observation. However most of his field-work was carried out in the Shetland Isles".

I was relieved to be back on course talking about otters, but I was not sure that Storm had followed my conversation . Was her mind still lost in some far away situation that might have been? I waited patiently. Maybe this was the moment to call it a night. Meantime I considered Hans Kruuk's work. It had been typically painstaking, thorough and full of great detail and had been recently published. Indeed it had formed the basis of how Martha Holmes of the BBC's Natural History Unit originally approached the making of 'Otters the Truth'. But Kruuk's research was still based on the behaviour of only the Shetland community of otters. They have been evolving there according to the harsh climate of those windswept isles for thousands of years, but even in that relatively short period of time have, and still are, developing different behaviour patterns to most of the otters of mainland Britain.

Suddenly Storm drifted back. "In what ways are Shetland otters different?" she enquired.

"I'll explain that in a moment, but recently I heard from Eamon de Buitlear, a wildlife film maker, who lives and works in Ireland. He has not long finished making a film about otters on the west coast, and the local individuals there are no different in their behaviour from those in Shetland, most interestingly with the timing of their breeding. "

Storm was now stretched out on her back within her nest of dry straw and bedding, her right foreleg bent at the knee and the pads and toes tucked neatly behind her right ear. I knew she was unlikely to interrupt me for a while from that position.

I continued quietly. "Many Shetland islands are physically remote and their shores are now uninhabited except for the free roaming flocks of sheep, so the otters there can be regularly seen in daytime unlike your mother, who was always making use of the sparse light at dawn and dusk. Consequently the Shetland animals hold little fear of man who has wrought such havoc elsewhere in these islands, and indeed wherever else otters live in the world. Kruuk found their diurnal, or daytime behaviour easy to observe and to study accurately. He could measure exactly how long they remained under water, and could observe what food species they take at different depths and stages of the tides, and how those fish and shell-fish species vary in the otters' diet from season to season. Obviously otters in Shetland live an almost wholly marine existence, but Kruuk has shown that even in these beautiful northern summer isles, otters, importantly and critically, must have easy access to supplies of fresh water both for drinking and also for the necessary cleaning of their salt-laden coats.

However the most important evolutionary fact that sets Shetland otters apart is that the bitches cub in June. On the various islands and skerries, their holts are to be found amongst the rocks close to the seashore or in abandoned rabbit warrens on the higher ground. The bitches have mated with their chosen dog on their territory in late March, having waited until the harshness of the winter storms and blizzards have abated. So necessary as Kruuk's work has been towards a better understanding of how wild otters function individually, its overall value is tempered by his research being undertaken on the population of the most northerly and remote island archipelago in the UK. This group of animals has from the very nature of their isolation been immune from the problems your mother was facing seven years ago and eight hundred miles away on Exmoor close to the land of 'The Two Rivers'."

As my thoughts returned to Storm's mother, I glanced at the upside down heap that was Storm. She was lying alongside me on her towel as I was sat quietly very close to her. There was the occasional twitch; from time to time a foreleg was stretched and toes and pads were parted, but other than that movement there was just her gentle but persistent snoring. As so often before, I knew I would soon be leaving her to deep and distant ottery dreams. Perhaps tonight, and because of her emotional involvement in my relating of the *Tarka* story, I wondered whether in her subconscious she might be retracing her mother's ramblings, or even her grandmother's tracks in the upper reaches of the Torridge watershed.

I had wanted to remind Storm in our discussion of another person whose generosity had greatly contributed to the study of otters. Vincent Weir's organisation has carried out major surveys on the status of the otter after the crash in numbers during the '50s. These provided vital evidence, pinpointed problems and thus indicated possible ways to stimulate the otters' recovery. The Vincent Wildlife Trust must also take the credit both for the introduction and the continuing success of the Otter Haven Project. This involves the creation of artificial holts. They are constructed out of a combination of concrete blocks and timber, both above and below ground-level, in an area surrounded by log piles and ground cover. These artificial resting and lying up areas offset the shortfall caused by the destruction of trees and vegetation, the otters' natural cover and one of the contributory causes to their sudden decline. Geoff Liles, with whom Storm and I have worked closely, was originally sponsored by the Trust and presently he continues with his 'Otters in Wales' work pursuing to the full, and with the cooperation of landowners, the policy of establishing a network of artificial holts. I know Vincent Weir has been totally absorbed for many years by the wildness and beauty of otters; it was both that and also their sudden vulnerability from the mid-'50s that prompted him to give time, energy and financial resources to their cause.

Now Storm was fast asleep I would relate to her the full story of the work of the Vincent Wildlife Trust on another occasion, as I would another fascinating detail, that might be causal to the release programme, conducted by the Otter Trust throughout the past twenty years, and which Helen and I have been privileged to support.

Philip Wayre's ambition was fired by the dramatic memories of his first wild otter on the Stiffkey marshes in the 1930s At dawn on a fine morning and well hidden by sea lavender, the otter surfaced beneath him in the creek. I wanted Storm to realise that Philip's first brief glimpse occurred some sixty years ago, while just over thirty years ago I had collected my first orphaned cub from the Salthouse marshes, no distance away in otter mileage. Was that cub's mother and therefore my first cub a direct descendant of the one seen by Philip Wayre? It was not beyond the realms of possibility.

For now the unbroken sound of Storm's gentle snoring was dominant in the quietness of the night. Inevitably too, my thoughts drifted to my first glimpse of a wild otter cub. So clearly in my mind was the small cardboard box next to the all night-stove and that little brown body snuggled within Bob's fisherman's sweater. So also was how I subsequently and memorably watched her parents and siblings amongst the remoteness of the tidal creeks in that brooding marsh of the north Norfolk coast. My memories of those many years past were swift, so swift as if in a dream. From Salthouse, I was then looking at Storm for the first time in another cardboard box, close to another all-night stove in the Burrows kitchen, high in the Quantock hills. Finally I could see her curled up asleep in the same box during those first days with Roger and Wendy.

Now I am actually staring at her. She's still so unbelievably close to me, and I am imagining her as a wild adult bitch asleep in a remote underground holt, even close to her mother's birthplace of several years previously. Thirty years ago my first cub, sixty years ago Philip's first sighting, seventy years ago the wild cub that was to become Williamson's Tarka in the epic story. Could Storm's mother, and therefore Storm herself be a great, great, great grand-daughter, a direct descendant of the otters of the land of 'The Two Rivers'? Although unlikely, it was a thrilling thought to take to bed and, excitingly, it really was not beyond the realms of possibility.

Why otters swim under water but close to the surface

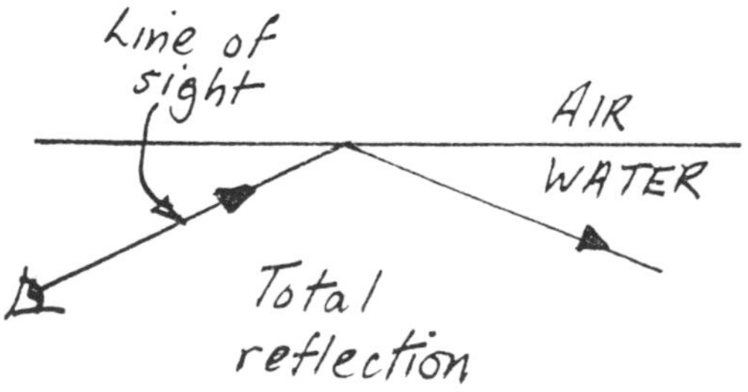

Diagram 5

196

Several nights passed before circumstances at home with Helen and Olivia allowed me another long and late stay with Storm. Over the years she has come to expect my regular visits, and the affection she has continually shown never ceases to amaze me. Whilst I am relaxing and enjoying time with Olivia, or maybe when I am reading or writing, I suddenly remember time and again that Storm is a truly wild animal whose trust is freely given. Sasha, our English Springer Spaniel, who has been with us now for four years after a couple of previous owners, is totally committed to our family. With her tail wagging constantly, she reacts so spontaneously, so explosively, to every movement in our home. Whether it is going out, feeding time, or joining Helen to carry and fetch Olivia to and from the pick-up point for the school bus, her time clock, aided by her previous attention to every detail of our movements, means that she is almost inevitably in advance of the actual event happening. On the other hand, Holly our cat, nurtured and raised by Helen as a farm stray and now past her ninth birthday, is affectionate in her own and different manner. Her time clock similarly impressive, and is also linked to our everyday routines. However, Holly remains quiet and rather aloof.

Last night, Storm's welcome and play was spontaneous and affectionate. I first spotted her deep in her bedding. Inevitably she was upside down and half asleep. I ran the fingers of one hand over her tummy as I knelt beside her, at the same time gently calling her name in rapid succession, "Storm, Storm, Storm."

She wriggled contentedly for a while but was soon pressing her front legs against the back of my hand. Perhaps she was recalling from long ago the once comforting and satisfying sensation of suckling her mother's milk-laden nipples. Meanwhile, after tickling her rudder, her play immediately became more boisterous. She then twisted and turned on her shoulders and the upper part of her back. At times like this, I keep my hands clenched and my fingers tight together, which leads to her chewing on my knuckles. Storm never sets out to deliberately hurt, although affectionate play for her can still be rough and can result in her teeth leaving thin razor-like cuts. If I am caught unawares, these can be particularly painful on the fine skin between the fingers! So having gently knawed my knuckles, explored and pulled very determinedly at my smock and sweater, she hesitated for a few seconds, as if to challenge my response. None was forthcoming so she plunged back into the tank. Moments later she sprang out again, shimmered, drenched me with a shower of fine droplets of cold water, and started the routine of her game all over again.

Sometimes I sit bolt upright with my back against the side of her den, draw my legs up at the knees and if at the same time I also leave them slightly apart, I can create a series of tunnels and runs. I momentarily show part of my hand from one angle, and as Storm makes for it, I withdraw it, only to present it again at a different position and angle fractions of a second later. Then quite determinedly she will explore under my knees and under my thighs but all the time I give her only just enough room to do this. I feel her forcing her subtle body through whatever gap I allow her. I will suddenly run my fingers over her head and neck, and then, if she is in a generous mood, drag them persistently but softly along her flat muzzle to her flat forehead and tickle her around the back of her ears. More often than not, she will come to lie in my lap and stay drooped over my knees. I eventually close them together as I become aware of her tiring. Finally, I will tickle her tummy and the pads of her feet yet again, and after a while she will roll over again into her favourite upside down position.

I would pursue these pastimes with her for hours, when she

Why otters swim under water but close to the surface

Otters need to know what is in the water in front of them. So they swim just under the surface of the water and look up at the surface at an angle which is smaller than the "critical angle". In this way, the otters see the reflection in the surface of the water of objects in the water in front of them (for example, fish) and also see the reflection of objects (such as rocks) which are on the bottom of the pond or river in which they are swimming. If an otter wishes to see what is above the surface of the water, all the otter needs to do is look upwards at an angle which is greater than the "critical angle" so that the otter's "line of sight" is similar to that shown in Diagram 3. A small inclination of the otter's head is all that is necessary if the otter wishes to change from looking out of the water to looking at the reflection of what is in the water. See page 214.

© Alan Duncan – O'Connor, Australia

first returned from the vital period spent with Roger and Wendy. Now, although she is far more experienced and cunning, a sense of exasperation can still creep into her play. So then I move gradually at what I feel is the right moment, and sit on a chair which is always next to her den. Inevitably she will immediately jump directly into my lap and the whole process will start all over again. Eventually, however, she does tire and goes to sleep tightly curled up in a ball, like Holly, our cat. Even after countless nights of Storm's very intimate company, I still have to remind myself that this large bundle of sleek brown fur is no ordinary puss, but an adult female British otter. Her devotion is quite amazing.

Tonight the bundle is slowly unwinding and stretching in front of me, and toes are being splayed on all four feet. She is yawning and now, finally, she is scratching very vigorously. Every movement on every night is carried out in precisely the same order. Of course that's no different from us. When we awake, it's straight into the bathroom, followed by cleaning teeth, washing and brushing hair. Then for many of us it's a cup of tea, for some it's several! We love and yet require the routine, we feel comforted by it and within it, and a wild otter, with no outside pressures and distractions, is no exception.

"You already know something about Nick Gordon," I started, taking up where I planned to brief Storm on some of the renowned photographers, who stalk the world's wild otters. "I have already read you his most recent letter just forwarded from his base camp in the Amazonian rainforest."

"He's finished filming 'Tarantulas and Giant Brazilian Otters', and recorded some of his exploits in a book as well, hasn't he?" murmured Storm drowsily. Storm was still in the lengthy process for Storm of coming around after several hours sleep. "Olivia mentioned you had bought her the book; she said she might read parts of it to me, the photographs are meant to be superb," continued Storm.

"That's right. His latest and final project for Anglia Television's 'Survival' series in South America is all about obtaining footage on jaguars. Sadly he will not be home for a while yet, but then I believe he will finally stay, living in his favourite place, which is on the island of Mull off the west coast of Scotland."

"I overheard Olivia saying to you not so long ago that she wanted to see his daughter Emma again."

"Yes, they write to one another and have done so since her father visited Helen and myself in Somerset. Nick was presenting the first of a couple of lectures for us. He showed marvellous and unique footage on both occasions. There were excerpts from his production 'Tiwai Island of Apes', filmed in west Africa, and of course, because of the audience's interest in otters, breathtaking footage of seven foot long giant Brazilian otters taking on fourteen foot Cayman alligators who had intruded their territories".

"Wow!" Storm was now quickly on board with the story. "Your guests must have loved seeing that".

"You bet, but when they experienced in tight close up and in full technicolour, the sequence of a giant Brazilian otter catching and eating a red piranha fish many of our friends and guests were put completely off their supper."

"So is that when Olivia first met Emma?"

"Yes, Emma came with her father and she's also accompanied him to his Amazon base-camp on a couple of occasions now."

"She's very lucky to be able to experience a tropical rain-forest," exclaimed Storm.

"Yes she is, but she has to endure long periods of time when she is unable to see her father. I miss Olivia terribly, when I am away just for a day or two, so imagine how Nick and Emma feel being apart for months at a time.

"You miss me too, don't you?" interrupted Storm rather anxiously.

"Of course. You're never very pleased when I can't see you for a few days, and I know that Olivia becomes upset too. Nick will make up for lost time with Emma when he comes home for good," I said reassuringly. "However to become acknowledged as one of the foremost wildlife cameramen, particularly specialising in the wildlife of the world's rainforests, requires considerable self-sacrifice on a scale I would not contemplate. There are many very difficult personal decisions and choices to make as he balances his priorities. But whilst talking about outstanding cameramen, I must tell you abut Hugh Miles."

"I think you have mentioned him briefly in the past. Didn't he go to Shetland for otters as well as Hans Kruuk?" said Storm.

Storm, when necessary, has a very good memory. Olivia has too, but not always at homework time!

"Hugh Miles's otter project was commissioned by Dilys Breeze, a producer in the Natural History Unit in Bristol. Presented with a real challenge and given that otters are so elusive, Hugh took it on with typical total enthusiasm and commitment. He spent three years close to a wild bitch otter, and amazingly finally became accepted by her on her own stretch of territory. He was closely advised by Bobby Tulloch, who had built up a great knowledge of the movements of local otter families and the other resident wildlife of Burraness, and the adjacent skerries of Basta Voe. Sadly Bobby passed away recently. He was highly respected and his knowledge of Shetland wildlife will be forever greatly missed."

"I thought Hugh Miles completed his film a long time ago".

"Yes, you are right, in the early 80s, and simultaneously his book on otters was published too."

"Has Hugh Miles made other films like Nick?"

"Yes and has achieved a series of major successes. He is now one of the most respected and sought after wildlife film makers. He will be remembered by many for 'Kingdom of the Ice Bear' which he made in Svalbard in 1984 with Mike Salisbury, another of the BBC's Natural History Unit's producers. Then there was 'Osprey' which he completed for the RSPB."

"Ospreys are another of the successful hunters of fish," commented Storm, "and like us, they're at the head of a food chain too," she added purposefully but in her usual friendly tone. She continued moments later. "What was his otter film called?"

"I am not sure I am right but probably *Shetland Otter*," I replied, "although his compelling book which accompanied the programme was entitled *On the Tracks of the Wild Otter*. As good and equally evocative and haunting was his *Flight of the Condor* series; marvellous footage of these vultures with their ten foot wing-span riding the thermals of the high massifs of the Andes. This range of mountains, home to some exceptional animals and birds, hugs the coast the length of the western seaboard of South America from the forest-covered heights of the equatorial north to Tierra del Fuego, the 'Land of Fire' in the far south. Then you are not that far from Antarctica and those penguins you seem to know so much about."

"So, like Nick, his work takes him from continent to continent."

"Strange we should be talking about Hugh Miles right now, but I gather from a recent magazine article that the fruits of his latest two year sojourn living in a tent in the mountains of Chile are about to be realised. His film on pumas was shown recently on the BBC's 'Natural World' series. For his latest project, the stills cameraman was Laurie Campbell, and he's another person who has taken plenty of very good otter photos in Scotland."

"I guess there are other wildlife cameramen to talk about but can we do that another time?" enquired Storm. "Can we talk about the future tonight? Can you tell me of your plans and what we are going to do together?" Storm was anxious to look forward to the weeks and months ahead.

"Yes of course, Storm, and talking to you about that will help clear my mind on an important subject."

"I will listen, but I am so tired I expect I will only interrupt occasionally."

"Not interrupting regularly will be a first for you," I joked.

With that, Storm settled herself in precisely the way she wanted in my lap. But just when I thought she was satisfied with her carefully prepared position, and I was on the point of altering my balance to accommodate her, Storm completed yet another half turn. However, she finally appeared to be content to stay for a long period upside down. I ran my fingers under her chin, and she pressed the pads of her front into the palms of my hands.

It was hard to know where to begin. To explain our future work could take a while, and therefore I wanted Storm to hear me out, before I lost her completely to her sleep. However I started by looking back at what had been successful in the past. From the many testimonials and letters of appreciation and thanks over the years, I knew my work had been well received by audiences, and it had achieved long-lasting and positive results, particularly for younger people. However, and frustratingly, it had never been easy to quantify that success.

"You know how I conclude my talks," I began quietly to Storm, "by making use of one or two quotations. The first, and I will repeat it to you now, is, 'in today's world of high consumption and overpopulation, it is essential to keep in touch with the earth, its changing seasons, its natural rhythms, its beauty and its mysteries; in fact nothing will suffice short of teaching youngsters to love nature and to love life'. That comes from 'Sharing Nature with Children,' written by Joseph Conrad."

"Lovely," murmured Storm, "very appropriate".

"The second," I continued, "and which I also try to work into my concluding discussion about the environment are words credited to Neil Armstrong on the Apollo X1 space-flight. He called up Mission Control in Houston, Texas, from the moon and said *'there is only one earth'*. In fact, his words were rather flippantly acknowledged. But moments later Armstrong was back to them and this time the whiplash was in the tail as he added *'and there's no spare one either'*."

"That's very true, " added Storm ," and where are otters going to go, and what are we going to eat when the marshes are drained, and the rivers and seas are stripped of their fish stocks?"

"You see, Storm, the message I need to put across time and time again in our presentations together is contained in the words of those two quotes. So let's look at them in more detail.

High consumption," I continued. "We know we use too much of everything. For example, few of my generation are going to give up the status symbol of excessive car ownership. We prefer to ignore the present and long-term pollution problems associated with that. Millions of people in this country, as the many more millions of people around the world, will continue to use the world's resources to excess. By that, they become increasingly divorced from, and separated from, the world natural. I could give you many examples, but here's one graphic case told to Helen and myself a few years back.

The details were related to us by Dr John Sparks. He used to be Head of the BBC Natural History Unit in Bristol, but now produces wildlife documentaries on a freelance basis. One of his best and most recent series was called 'Realms of the Russian Bear'. The film took him and his camera team three years to complete throughout the several time zones that encompass the vast landmass of the old Soviet Republics. These stretch across the northern hemisphere in the mainly high latitudes, from the Atlantic Ocean in the west to the Pacific Ocean in the east. When needing to work in the northern and eastern side of the vast mountain ranges of the Himalayas, he and his crew would need access via Japan. He finally obtained lovely footage from Lake Baikal, a landlocked inland sea where the only freshwater seal in the world lives. There were breathtaking scenes from high mountain ranges, where as they strained to obtain film of snow leopards, you felt that probably no other living soul had previously set foot there. Finally there was remote Kamchatka, a sparsely populated peninsula on the eastern Pacific seaboard, where they finally obtained pictures of the Eurasian otter.

Whilst passing through Tokyo on one occasion, he visited the capital's fish market, which he described to Helen and myself as being unbelievably large. Then, with fear in his voice, he said

'David, you should also see the expanse of the tuna fish market alone. The Pacific Ocean will never sustain yielding that quantity of fish without destroying, much sooner rather than later, the breeding stocks for the future; and when you think," he added, obviously still very upset, "that the Japanese harvest those tuna by using all embracing fine nets, sometimes up to 50 miles long....."

At that moment I heard Storm gasp in disbelief.

".....from which nothing else can escape," I added. "Imagine the sea turtles, the many and various species of seabirds, and the dolphins trapped and drowned just to satisfy the demands of the Japanese markets. We do practically nothing, internationally, to stop it. You can understand John Sparks' emotion and sadness, as he told Helen and myself of an experience witnessed by an exceptional naturalist, who cares so much. This is a story which needs to be repeated time and time again."

"We seem to be turning a blind eye to some pretty nasty situations happening around the world, don't we. Why is that?"

"Long story Storm, with each one needing a detailed yet different explanation, but I suppose the plight of your otter family worldwide summarises the circumstances accurately. There are some horrendous examples of man's persecution, of his pollution and of his destruction of habitats worldwide and therefore the loss of the creatures living within those particular environments. I could cite any number, but just now off the top of my head, I will mention as examples, the ongoing dramatic decline of tigers in India, of pandas in China, the mountain gorillas of Rwanda, the monk seals of the eastern Mediterranean, the list is endless. We do know however, that the infiltration by chemical residues to the head of the food chains has, for example, manifested itself in the breeding colonies of penguins in Antarctica."

"Those bleak parts are far too cold for crops to be grown. So how come? " insisted Storm.

"Remember," I replied, "that these chemicals have been used extensively in the wheat and maize growing prairie states of America, North and South Dakota, Nebraska, Kansas and Oklahoma, all of which are drained by the Missouri River and its tributaries. The chemicals are discharged into the Caribbean currents and soon they are within fish species, which in turn migrate into oceanic currents. See the connection coming? Penguins may breed in Antarctica or on its adjacent islands and archipelagoes, the Falklands, South Georgia, Graham Land and

204

so on, all the various places I have mentioned to you before. They may bring up their young in the long hours of daylight of the southern ocean's short summer, but when old enough and with their parents, they flee the onset of the polar winter and migrate on currents thousands of miles to other oceans and seas whose fish are carrying the deadly residues."

"Its quite unbelievable," gasped Storm again. "Are you saying the whole world is polluted?"

"Yes, and another point, Storm, is that, even though in this country we have many internationally respected naturalists, and we make possibly the best wildlife documentary films in the world, we still have just as many problems facing our own environment at home. Obviously, they are on a lesser scale; however, it means that it is very difficult for us to tell others what to do, when our own house is nowhere near in order."

"Are you saying that it's something to do with the phrase, 'people who live in glass houses'?"

"That's right, and while you are in the business of finding phrases to fit, here's another, 'money talks' or rather, 'money counts'."

"Go on then, explain briefly," said Storm.

I noted she said 'briefly'.

"Some of the largest companies in the world responsible for the pollution and destruction of the world's environments are British owned or British based, employing many thousands of people. They feel it is not in their employees', or shareholders', interests to cut their own throats, so to speak, by acting more responsibly, if their competitors aren't either. So we contribute to the problem that I have just been describing, and it's going to take a great deal of soul searching and self sacrifice to alter that situation. But alter it we must, and sooner rather than later."

"How do you think we should at least make a start?" Storm sounded rather desolate.

In fact, I felt I could now concentrate just on one particular issue with Storm, and it would present the perfect example of how the United Kingdom could tackle an international problem, give an international lead to its solution and thus gain respected international standing on a critical global wildlife issue.

"Over the years, there have been a series of oil disasters both around our shores and elsewhere in the world resulting in great losses to sealife and with inestimable long term destruction to marine environments. The tanker *Torrey Canyon*'s oil spill was the first major incident in this country in 1967. I remember driving to Cornwall from my wildlife park in Bristol with a friend Tim Appleton, who was then a member of my staff, to collect some 60 or so oiled guillemots and razorbills. I am sorry to say that our efforts to try and clean them were very unsuccessful; no satisfactory cleaning techniques had been effectively worked out at that time. For a long time afterwards, I was saddened by the birds' obvious suffering and distress. Incidentally the tanker had gone aground on the Seven Stones Reef close to the Isles of Scilly, not thirty miles as the crow flies from where we are sitting at this moment. It seems that, at intervals of every few years, yet another ever larger super-tanker inevitably comes to grief in an area of great importance to seabird life. On every occasion, hundreds of volunteers collect, clean and eventually return a few survivors to the wild. The story makes for sympathetic headlines in the national press for a few days, an inquiry is promised by the government, legislation and corrective procedures are even hinted at, but successively the dreadful demise is repeated. The names of the ships and the associated havoc wreaked on the adjacent coastline and shores roll off the tongue. In 1978 the *Amoco Cadiz* off Brittany, in 1989 the *Exon Valdez* in Alaska, where the population of sea otters was decimated, and most recently, and within your short lifetime, the *Braer* was aground in Shetland in January 1993. Finally in March 1996 the *Sea Empress* struck the rocks off St Ann's Head in Pembrokeshire, as she entered the oil terminal and refinery at Milford Haven."

"That's very close to those seabirds islands you were telling me about, Grassholm...."

".....where the gannets live," I interrupted, "fifteen thousand pairs there at least....."

"Skomer where your friend Ronald Lockley lived and studied the manx shearwaters, and where the puffins nest; don't otters live in an estuary near there?"

"Yes they do; or rather I think they winter in the tidal creeks of the Haven but, in summer, they breed further upstream, on tributaries of both the Cleddau rivers. Their sources are further inland in the Preseli Hills."

"So are you saying that stopping tanker disasters is down to us in this country?" enquired Storm further.

"No, not altogether of course," I replied, "for there must be an international response as well. However, there are many British companies closely involved with the oil industry. In fact, we are one of the world's major producers. Our crude oil comes from the North Sea and Shetland fields, so an innate responsibility goes with both extracting and transporting the raw material. Yet money and profits are the name of the game. When the *Braer* went aground and was smashed to pieces on the Shetland shore, she had been taking a short cut in bad weather in 70 or 80 mile an hour winds. She was far too close to one of the most populated and most varied concentrations of breeding seabirds and other wildlife in the northern hemisphere."

"What happened?" Storm was well with the story as it unfolded.

"She suffered total engine failure and drifted under the cliffs. But not before a delay of several hours caused by the arguments over salvage meant that it had been left too late for a rescue tug to be given a chance to pull her clear."

"That's pretty irresponsible, isn't it?" Storm was adamant.

"At least a salvage tug was on hand," I added rather sarcastically. "The then Conservative Government had been promising that tugs would be strategically and permanently placed on station in key areas, in order to be on immediate call in case of just such an emergency. One would be close to us here, in Mounts Bay or Falmouth Roads to cover the South Western Approaches and the Isles of Scilly."

"To prevent another *Torrey Canyon*," interrupted Storm.

"That's right, and another would be stationed in Milford Haven, close to the oil terminal and refinery there and ready to assist, if a laden tanker were to come to grief for whatever reason close to the seabird islands."

"And did they have the tugs ready?"

No, the one in the English Channel was on station, but the Milford Haven super-tug had not been placed and in the late winter of 96 the super-tanker the *Sea Empress* became stuck fast on rocks at the entrance to the oil refinery. By the time a large enough tug had arrived to pull her clear a week later, most of her cargo, seventy thousand tons in fact, had spilt from her ruptured tanks.

"Did many birds die?" Storm enquired with an obvious hint of sadness.

"Luckily, after going aground, much of her cargo of crude oil dispersed before the main flocks of wintering auks returned from the open Atlantic Ocean. However, since it was still late winter, great rafts of sea-ducks, which summer in Iceland and further north and which come south on migration to the sheltered waters in the good shellfish feeding grounds of St Bride's Bay, were still overstaying, along with the resident populations of cormorants, shags, and Atlantic grey seals. There were flocks of up to fifteen thousand scoter ducks, but sadly as many as five thousand perished."

"So what can we do?" Storm sounded desperate.

"I must tell you, Storm, that inevitably money and politics play their evil but significant role in any potential solution," I continued. "You will find that matters will only improve when it suits one of the major players in the game. Unfortunately that begins to explain how, when we feel we need to see conservation measures taking place in other countries, others can really always point an accusing finger at us, and, as I have mentioned before, often with much justification"

"How are we going to change that in any way?" Storm was still anxious.

"I was hoping you might realise the answer to that question yourself," I added. " In a very small way, I think what we set out to achieve in our lectures together can generate a shift in opinions. Oil companies *will* be made to change their minds, government legislation *will* arrive, people *will* become one car families and a new generation *will* mature into sensible parents, with a wholly different respect for Planet Earth. Youngsters, Storm, need to be shown, advised and ultimately warned time and time again, that Planet Earth has limited and finite natural resources, and that Planet Earth cannot sustain, in any way, those resources current rate of destruction."

"There's only one earth and no spare one either. Armstrong was absolutely right, wasn't he?" enthused Storm.

"Don't forget," I added quickly noting Storm's now perkier attitude, "that it is your presence, close to enquiring and impressionable young minds, which can be the catalyst that gives the incentive for such vital changes. You can have organisations like Greenpeace who are marvellously drawing attention to major worldwide issues, or the RSPB, now with a million members, who are acquiring national reserves for all time from its now vast financial resources built up by public donations....."

".....Then there are the specialist organisations you have mentioned," interrupted Storm enthusiastically, "the Wildfowl and Wetlands Trust, and the Otter Trust. Isn't there a Hawk Trust as well?"

Storm was still sorting out the various organisations but I was more concerned with the major players in the field.

"There are the wildlife television series made by the BBC's Natural History Unit and by ITV's Survival," I continued. "Producers and cameramen such as John Sparks, Hugh Miles and Nick Gordon, all three of whom I have mentioned, can captivate millions in their armchairs with the results of their latest safari abroad. But I will tell you for certain Storm, that just one hour of you in front of the younger members of the audience as in Brecon can be as influential, memorable and important as any fifty minute programme on prime-time television. I have brought you one of the letters I received after that successful night, from the 'Griffiths' family of Pontypool, and forwarded just a few days later."

I read the contents to Storm who was now well alert. The tragedies of oil spillages and of their damaging and devastating aftermath, particularly on her own kind in Alaska, Pembrokeshire and in the Northern Isles had aroused her from her usual nocturnal slumber. 'We considered meeting Storm a great privilege for our family' were the final words of their letter.

"So you can see," I continued, "I know that's the way ahead for us. The success of my wildlife park thirty years ago was reached on the basis of enthusing young people. It was vital then as world-wide pollution began to rear its ugly head. Although much progress has been made, more and more problems are now arising, mainly because of the continued surge in the world's population."

"I didn't know there *were* more and more people in this country."

"Our population is growing only slowly, but even here we still continue to take in large tracts of green countryside for more housing and factories, instead of making use of the existing waste and redundant land in the inner cities. So imagine the pressure on the countryside and all the accompanying pollution in countries such as India, China and parts of Africa, and south and central America where population growths are continuing to rise steadily. Then the problem does indeed become quite frightening."

"So I can see why you say 'in today's world of high consumption and over-population'."

"Therefore the great need, if we are going to make our influence felt, as we surely must soon, is to get our act together here in this country first. That means young people growing up

209

and going out into the world with a more unselfish attitude towards the planet that gives them their life. Hopefully we can change attitudes for the better by combining with the enlightened young people of European countries. We could produce a groundswell movement, a tide of enthusiasm and imagination which might, perhaps, then gain momentum worldwide and help protect the planet from the worst of the pollution catastrophes building up on the horizon."

"Save the rainforests of South America, especially in the Amazon Basin where Nick is working, or in Africa, and the Congo River and its uplands where the mountain gorillas are under such threat......"

"....or wherever rain forests are," I interrupted, "in the Far East, Malaysia and so on......"

".....protect Antarctica from any exploitation," continued Storm enthusiastically. "If we were to allow drilling for oil in that last unspoilt wilderness, then, given time, there will surely be a major disaster."

"I am afraid so, especially if we don't take the lead in this country and create a high standard of protection and code of conduct around our own coasts. That could become a blue-print, provide the stepping stones to an overall protection plan, which is required sooner rather than later and has to be accepted on an international scale."

"There are those chemicals associated with intensive farming. They are washed out into streams and ditches where wild otters hunt on the local fish stocks. There's the overfishing in the coastal seas at the mouth of estuaries, where they live in winter-time, the list is endless," sighed Storm. "It is really quite depressing, isn't it?"

I moved quickly before Storm disappeared into a whole catalogue of problems, into a downward spiral which is inevitable, when anyone seriously reflects on our ongoing savaging of the natural resources that belong to everybody and every living creature. So, finally, I thought I would concentrate on one particular world-wide resource under threat. However, at the same time, I would give her positive ideas to consider when I eventually left her. I would leave the more complicated description of imminent problems with worldwide consequences, such as global warming, carbon-dioxide emissions and the destruction of the ozone layer over Antarctica, and all recently dicussed by delegates at an international conference in Kyoto,

Japan, for another occasion.

"Let's concentrate on the wetlands of the world." I stressed. "As you have mentioned, they hold the all-important estuaries, rivers and waterways, complimented by a multitude of inter-dependent communities in their adjacent marshes and swamps. Your friends live in those places here, and throughout the world. Before you interrupt to tell me again that the outlook is so bleak that it seems pointless trying to alter the situation, let me remind you that there are very many people worldwide putting the important messages across to younger people. I am one of those people, who has already and still tries to continue to influence, thanks in no small part by the role you can and do play with me."

"Surely our book 'Stormforce' will help too?" Storm questioned.

"Of course and you know that I have been writing our story for some while now, always recording our conversations and thoughts. Tonight's discussion will be no different. In fact I am planning it to be part and parcel of the concluding chapter. I wanted to bring you right up to date and to explain the enormity of the problem, and although I have suffered a setback in health, I am really only content in mind when I am pursuing what I believe to be my valuable and necessary work."

"I enjoy being with you as well," replied Storm happily, "and especially with Olivia. I still can't believe my luck in finding you as a family."

There was a long pause as I watched her, and I sensed she had more to add.

"I wish I could tell my family everything that has happened, particularly my mother. I hope they are all okay, living in a good place and that they are safe."

"I am sure they are. I expect by now at least one of your brothers will have a family of his own, and both could well have wandered a considerable distance from the holt where you were born."

I was anxious not to discuss the many pitfalls that face all family groups of otters, otherwise I could find myself talking about possible tragedies, which might or might not have occurred. For Storm's story is a happy one and I wanted to look forward positively with her.

"Do you realise the time?" I continued, "time I went and had at least a few hours sleep tonight. But just before I go, I must bring you up to date with some rather sad news, before I tell you the good news. There are people all over the world working for the environment each in their own way, and who tackle the problems from their totally different backgrounds. Tragically somebody who had created his own charitable conservation foundation in the United States was killed recently. He crashed whilst piloting his own plane. His name was John Denver. His charity was working towards what he called 'a sustainable future for the Earth', which is a sort of academic way of describing our conversation tonight. He made his name and money by writing and singing folk songs extremely well, and his music and lyrics were appreciated worldwide by millions of people. But he was also using his money to make practical conservation work. So someone else who would have continued to exert great influence towards a better planet, both through his music and his dedication, has been lost."

"That's so distressing," sighed Storm, "such an unnecessary waste."

"But the good news," I hurried on, "is that we're back out together again shortly, this time for Wiltshire Wildlife Trust.

"Where are we going, and what are we going to be doing this time?" Storm's enthusiasm was rapidly on the up again, even though it was now the middle of the night.

"We are promoting, or rather you are going to promote to be precise, the construction of artificial holts for wild otters."

"Geoff Liles organises that throughout Wales."

"That's right, except this time it is Thames Water who are funding the Wiltshire Trust's holt building programme on the upper reaches of the tributaries of the River Thames, close to the Avon and Kennet Canal.

"Is it wise for you to continue working?"

"With other work in the pipeline I shall be more selective in future," I cautioned, "and will make sure we don't work under the same pressures as before. When away, we will certainly stay overnight more often."

"It's really good news, isn't it, especially as there is such an important job to be done. Meanwhile, you *must* finish writing the manuscript for the book."

Suddenly Storm had a new lease of life and was her eager self again.

"Yes, I must," I replied. "I knew that if I didn't leave soon I would find myself waking up again in the early hours with a wet otter in my lap."

Storm had been rigorously rolling on her towel, obviously

excited at the thought of accompanying me on another expedition, but now paused, as I continued.

"You remember I told you about Hugh Miles and the otters he filmed in Shetland. He wrote at length about an individual bitch otter, whom over the three years at Basta Voe he grew to recognise by her unique facial markings. He regularly filmed her in her favourite places on her territory, either when she was fishing or when resting and grooming, or even when she was occasionally with her mate, the dog. He filmed at her holt and the first time she brought out her twin cubs to the foreshore, so as to introduce them gradually to the rise and fall of the tides and the vagaries of the open sea . I remember the boy cub was quite bold, but the little girl was shy and timid."

"Just like me," said Storm quietly.

"Yes, she turned away and ran back to the safety of the holt." At that moment I was tempted to ask Storm if that was the real reason why she became separated from her mother all that time ago. On second thoughts, I hastened on.

"One day the wild bitch came ashore as usual very close to Hugh. It was an occasion when he knew where she would be, having long understood how her everyday behaviour and business was linked to the ebb and flow of the tides. In turn, she had grown to tolerate his presence. He had never interrupted her, and her confidence had grown in him. But, on this occasion, with only perhaps two or three days of his contract left before he finally departed the Shetland shores, instead of passing him by, she turned and came towards him. She hesitated and then stood, just briefly, up against him on her hind legs."

"And he took some brilliant close-ups," interrupted Storm.

"No, far from it. He still pretended to work the film camera on its tripod, and although he felt her presence extremely close to him, he never attempted any sudden movement in order not to break her trust. Quickly she was gone, slipping away to go about her life. Marvellous, wasn't it? It was as if she had come to say good-bye. He told me this story when I was in the studios of the BBC in Bristol, recording with Tony Soper for a children's wildlife programme called 'Wildtrack'. I had my triplet cubs of the year with me and Hugh was editing *Shetland Otter*. I took the cubs upstairs to the cutting-room, so that he could compare the age and size of my cubs with the wild youngsters he had captured on film coming to the shoreline with their mother."

"That wild female of his, she reminds me so much of my mother....." added Storm thoughtfully."

213

Why otters swim under water but close to the surface

Otters swim close to the surface of the water so that they can see the objects in the water which are fairly close to them. If they swam well below the surface, they would see reflections in the surface of the water of the objects that are quite far away from them. Any attempt by an otter which is swimming deep to see nearby objects in the water would result in the otter's "line of sight" meeting the surface of the water at an angle which is greater than the critical angle for reflection, and the otter would see only objects that are above the surface of the water. Such a situation is shown in Diagram 6.

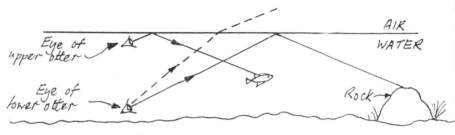

Diagram 6

In this situation the upper otter would be able to see clearly the fish that is swimming a short distance ahead of the otter. The lower otter would be unable to see any object in the water that is closer to the rock. Which otter do you think would be more likely to catch the fish?

© Alan Duncan – O'Connor, Australia

Suddenly there was a sharp knock on the outer door of Storm's den. It took us both by surprise.

"I thought you might have fallen asleep again." It was Helen and she seemed excited. "A while back Ken was on the phone from the Tamar Otter Sanctuary to say that Pebble must have cubbed around dawn today. He's already heard strong squeaking from the cub or cubs. He also said that, on the advice of Philip Wayre he has left the dog, I forget his name, in with her. Something about it may help Pebble settle during the first critical days. Anyway, it's brilliant news isn't it? Are you on your way indoors now? Oh, hello Storm, and bye bye Storm, talk to you next time."

Almost as quickly as she had arrived Helen was away into the darkness. I called after her, "I am about to finish with Storm and then lock up. Give me another five minutes with her."

I could see Storm was equally happy about the news of Pebble, and then I immediately realised I was going to find it very difficult to settle her quickly. However late, it would take more than the five minutes I had suggested to Helen.

"First Ripple, now Pebble, both Cider and Blackthorn would have been thrilled. That's the third time she has given birth now," added Storm excitedly.

"And hopefully third time lucky," I replied immediately.

Storm had dipped into her tank, tumbling over and over in a characteristic display of happiness, and I reflected briefly on Pebble. She deserves the breaks to bring the cubs through, I thought to myself. 'Be another lucky otter,' I whispered quietly, but my words were lost against the noise of Storm plunging time and time again like a dolphin. Once Storm had hauled herself back onto her towel ready for a prolonged session of drying and stimulating her coat, I returned to my original story. She was now clearly very alert after her exhilarating swim, and I was determined to share some long standing thoughts with her before I went indoors.

"Hugh Miles also wrote that with his filming concluded, he had completed another assignment, but instead of relief and celebration, there was sadness, a privilege ended," I continued quietly. "He realised that he would probably never see his bitch otter again, never again experience the trust she shared with him. In short, he concluded his life would never be quite the same.

So Storm, now I want you to remember, and I know I speak for Helen and Olivia too, that your presence with us for the past seven and a half years represents everything that makes the 'world natural' so extraordinary for me. Every day I spend in your company is special. It's the same when I'm with Helen and particularly, when I'm with Olivia as she grows up. There is always something for me to treasure at nightfall. Remember, you have so much to offer for the future well-being of your fellow otters by being able to influence so many young people. Indeed John F Kennedy reminded us that '...Youngsters are the world's most valuable resource and still its best hope for the future.' So you can help persuade them to reverse the chemical craziness and short-sightedness of the past decades. Working with you and for otters everywhere makes me realise that with hard work there is still a light at the end of a very long tunnel, and the battle to ensure the survival of the 'world natural' from the pressures and the pitfalls of our polluted planet can still be won. I can remember a most relevant caption for a poster which highlighted the problems otters faced at the height of the crisis in the '50s. The words although admittedly taken out of context from

Shakespeare's *Merchant of Venice*, complimented a lovely close-up photo of the head of a dog otter. They read 'You do take my life when you do take the means whereby I live.' We must make sure those words will shortly no longer apply to the world's wetlands where otters live. So therefore for my life's work, I thank you".

I had not been as concise as I had planned, and I hoped that Storm had remained awake to hear my thoughts that were sincerely but which were, perhaps, rather inadequately expressed. Nevertheless they were words I had been meaning to say to her for a long time. Yes, although curled up on her towel, with her head lying across her forelegs as usual, I could still see the whites of her eyes as she watched me closely. I stroked her gently and for the last time that night. "I will read the final draft of '*Stormforce*' to you shortly," I said gently.

I closed and bolted the inner safety door. In those few seconds, my wild creature would be rapidly drifting away deep into her ottery dreams; maybe she would think of Ripple's triplets or of Pebble's new born cubs, on whom so much now depended; she might be remembering Blackthorn, Ripple's father, or dear old Cider, her erstwhile companion in her formative, and his latter years. Could I, in turn, find a dog otter of their style to share her future life? But, most of all, I reckoned that her thoughts at this moment would have again been of her own mother. The experiences of those first six weeks in the wild holt have, for sure, never left her.

I had not realised either, as I cast my final glance at her, that a strong wind had rapidly risen, and my face was quickly wet from the squalls of driving and heavy rain. Immediately I recalled yet again that wild Boxing Day night on Salthouse marsh over thirty years ago with my friends Bob and Joan, and my first otter cub in the cardboard box by the Aga stove where this great adventure had begun.

If ever I lose my sense of wonder, I thought to myself, I will lose my sense of perspective of life; if I lose that, well.....

"Good night, Storm," I called to my otter above the strengthening gale.

AFTERWORD.

Do wheels turn full circle?

I trust these notes will allow the reader through the back
door, as it were, and into the untidy workshop of my mind.
I believe the extra information although only briefly related,
will help to further animate the remarkable story of Storm. After
reading these details you may feel you now actually know this
marvellous creature.

The Stormforce manuscript was commenced at Old
Holt Farm on the Somerset Levels during the summer
of '96 and was, for the most part, concluded at
Wild Waters Holt in West Penwith, Cornwall by the
early spring of '99.

MEETING FRANK OWEN

Typical November's meat at 5° four in somerset. incessant heavy drizzle on the wind; obviously unable to go out with Storm so I've timed myself between a couple of straw bales. I am pressing to spend time with my mind.

Storm has taken half an hour exploring my old anorak coat. Now has the soft molten hues; she picks up the scent of him the other child I had fed earlier. She's seeming involved in some intent and aggressive play. I am trying to coax her to get up to talk. The only noise has been the occasional clang from the gutter outside of wind — the sound opposite. Otherwise it's just the steady sound of rain on the field shed.

Storm turns to me " Where did it all start then? You know how you've managed through the last 20-year with otters?

It comes from a love of wildfowl and waders and the places where they live. You know how much the sounds of the marshes meant to your mother + grandmother. — 5 "Night otters knowing intimately instant meaning matter of wigeon, teal. elsewhere surface at

BUT meeting Frank Owen reason for it goes back further ::

My first duckies — under garden 2 khaki C's + an Aylesbury, night before my birthday; wrote November night — similar + toasts, one more was unaware' my father waiting at me as we leaned reading the definite gnashing coming from up the garden.

Then my paternal grandmother hearing a 'Living Broadcast by Peter Scott from Severn Wildfowl Trust. Tell him Free' from that first visit 'I was hooked on wildfowl, the wildness of Slimbridge, so different from the Zoo. .

— & Storm interrupts — still haven't explained the connection to us otters. Starts, I reply, with a story that PS relates.

"Peter Scott was a wildfowler before the war, shooting ducks + geese for sport. But on one occasion a goose that he had only injured planed onto the sandflats, unable to take off. Although the gun dog was put out several times to retrieve the goose, he was unable to rescue it. PS later wrote that he was certainly saddened as he watched it 'head held proudly high', surrounded by the incoming rising tide. He had caused that birds slow death by drowning and became one of the first occasions when he (PS) started to wonder what so clever in shooting these wonderful birds.

Leaving Storm. They used to hunt your relation with dogs until 1979. individual otters outnumbered 30-40 to — in the name of sport too !!

However another thing had come through from Scott's shooting days; he thought he was able to identify a new species of goose from the specimens he had shot. But unfortunately people to whom he had presented his case were not impressed because of im use of skins. It wasn't until just after the war in 1947, along with a friend called Dalgety, that a committee accepted the Greenland White-fronted Goose; with the use of live birds. Now I had read about this and was determined to try and see them as they were only newly known to science. Although the great majority of the flocks in western Scotland and Ireland, there was a small isolated flock of some 60-70 birds that would come just that little bit further to spend the harshest time of the year on the Tregaron Bog in mid-Wales. I was determined to go there!

was that where you saw your first otter? Storm interrupts
"Hold on", I reply "I was still bowled over by mitreford & waders, a
up my own exhibition by now. But as the collection grew, yes so did
some going to mid-Wales, and ∴ the possibility of seeing my ?
although I was unaware of their special magic at the time.

Then my father acquired a cottage near Barmouth; it overlooked a beautiful
estuary — the Mawddach. The place was in disrepair, and as an architect, my
father had to go to supervise its reconstruction. I persuaded him to take me to
help with the measuring, and also to go the longer way, ie through mid-Wales,
and parts the Tregaron Bog.

we followed the valley of the River Teifi from Lampeter to Tregaron, almost
directly following the Milford Haven to Manchester railway line which had recently
been abandoned. Arrive came into the small market town we turned left on the
Abergwesyn road and was soon parked near a bridge under which the Teifi flowed
out of the Bog. Quite quickly I had seen my first teal in the shallows, & heard my the
haunting calls of the Curlew.

I realised how extensive the marsh was; the vegetation had the marvellous
tones of autumn. I knew already that I would have to come back to explore it further.
→ "I we were about half-way along the marsh when it happened"
      "What happened" interrupted Storm. "Did you suddenly see an otter?"
(I was surprised Storm was still listening; I really wanted her to understand too that
it was from P/S that I was learning that it the wild places where creatures live that had
to be protected as much as the animals themselves).
→ "So how 200 bantams — what's important about bantams?
I needed broody bantams to hatch my clutches of duck eggs. The bantams are light,
they don't crush the eggs & make good attentive mothers. I needed Silkie X (Cross) not
pure Silkie — not easy to find them. Suddenly there were more than I had ever seen.
I feasted my eyes on the flock, scanning the paddock, all sizes and colours. Suddenly
in the middle of them, I saw a goose, not a farmyard goose (Toulouse or Emden), but
a Barnacle, a solitary bird - the middle of nowhere in the midst of all the bantams.

we had to find out why! Nearest cottage called MAESLLYN — knocked on
the door and the man who introduced himself as FRANK OWEN answered — + the
rest is history.

_____

DEVELOP: FRANK O.   and WHY BARNACLES!
      1. Keeper of Teifi Pools   2) Yes there were G/W geese + yes P/S came to
watch them; who = adjacent valley   the Rheidol
                                                                ⟶ 3) Injured female (present was free Hbs)
                                                                       sent by a man who fished with
      I had bred a male.   F/O for him whose wife Elizabeth
      + I said I would take,   to look after.
      it to make a pair!

I felt as excited as Storm remembering some of the earliest, most evocative and romantic times I spent as a young naturalist. The Tregarron Bog has never lost, and will never lose, its uniqueness for me.

Did you take him the goose? (Storm) "Yes & I came back with some bantams"

'Develop bantam story', tiny ones to sit on Carolina & Mandarin — remember individuals. One dark bird with rich amber gold feathers; two pale yellow-golden birds with striking black fleck; another was fluffy — could only see her feet — legs invisible behind trouser-like feathers. (If leg-feathers stay wet after a shower — then ducklings, goslings in crop run risk of pneumonia) — describe how strange it is that 1 + x " bring on water can catch "

Finally two yellow ones used for Red-crested Pochard + Tufted (diving ducks) that lay larger eggs.

More bantams on a pond of time, added a couple every time I went! Learnt more about the Bog on every visit — the birds that nested = summertime, or there on migration in winter. more about the geese, the Red Kites (much more numerous today, buzzards + ravens took me to visit a school-teacher (PETER PAINTING) — lived = hamlet called Cellan (rambling the gorge high up off the lane) searching old house with Pied Flycatcher (nestbox scheme = woodland) built original district, knew about Pine Martens & Polecats

Storm interrupts: But what about the otter; did Frank Owen show you otters. No, never stayed long enough travelling to & from Bournemouth. But he did set out on on one occasion what he felt were the tell-tale signs which he had known for so long.

1). clearly said that it would be difficult
2) dog otters only on the Bog these they would seem quite freely.
3). what to pick up fresh water streams from the higher ground where at the same time there was plenty of cover — here the bitch otter would anchor her territory

Then he came out with most surprising statement
"What was that?" "Well, he said you want to find clear water cover and ...." , "Yes, yes, you've said all that"

Clear water & cover for the holt but close to a rabbit warren. Just like your mother did, high on Exmoor. She used to whip out of her holt for an easy feed on 1/4 rabbits. meat, full of protein, just what a pregnant bitch or your mum for that matter with her triplet cubs. No need to travel far from the holt, (ravens & red-kite Tregarron) for a buzzard on Exmoor), would clear up the left-overs at dawn.

Storm reply   Now you come to mention it we were close to rabbits. With my two brothers, I remember listening to them chattering amongst themselves he used to be frightened by them thumping their back legs on the ground when they were startled & wanted to warn each other.

— SO fresh meat VITAL & vital ingredient for a healthy family of Otters! DON'T SUPPOSE MANY PEOPLE KNOW THAT (develop = text later)

Sunday night late 23 March 96.

'STORM on TIGGER.'

'I heard him cry out — a stifled pain'
sodded Bramble Willow & B'thorn who are also distressed.

T pulls more bedding around him — a natural instinct to
stay warm and safe, but his food is left untouched.
No more whistling and squeaking and chattering to P/B/+W, compared
to his constant noise over the years past.

'he (T) tells them he doesn't think he will make it to Cornwall
this time. (previously attacks of ARTHRITIS — BAD TEETH & ABSCESSES + (signs of old age)
BLINDNESS (in right eye) How do wild otters cope? or in fact do they cope?!

Storm knows already because she has been told! that T & his
elderly and her dear friend CIDER will not be going either.
(others of journey)

After a few days of deep sleep — only interrupted by toilet
drinking and swimming and dragging in more dry bedding (daily routine
my instinct) T starts to eat a little tries and mackerel; cut very fine.
But T's heart attack has made him gaunt, a fact I can't believe the
change that took place in him overnight.

— — TIGGER

When young cub he was very
frightened of water, had to
be dragged in by the scruff of
his neck by his mother.

Grew to love his tank &
was never happier than when a hose
was being played into the water for
hours at a time.

Also spent most of his time checking
his enclosure, his house & when his
door was never properly bolted (you
would never guess the number of times I
forgot, top middle & bottom!) he
proceeded to mend it.

I comforted him, started giving him his pills as
begin to slow him down, to doing him to ease the
DAVID on 'TIGGER' nagging pain. I talked to him & he (Tigger)
quietly responded.

Tigger knew he was going to join his father / mother, and all the other
friends he had known, — those who had lived (and argued & did
he argue) with him; his cousins who had gone to the OT, & then to
live in the wild & subsequently & have bred & then sadly died in the wild.

"I've (Tigger) had a super life : all the food (and more) & fun
I've always wanted ; I'm sorry I've not got on with any of my girlfriends,
and therefore I've had no sons and daughters of my own. BUT I've
enjoyed being introduced to all your friends, being shown off, & indeed showing
off — that was my role, wasn't it, when the females were breeding, & the other
males (Severin, Clae etc) were too shy !

I'm sad I won't hear the Swifts again this summer. I was very
young, and mum was forever trying to bring me into the crate. I wasn't
very keen and then it was strange how fond I became of water & hoses !
When I first saw the Swifts & heard them screeching at dusk over our home
& the square sheds, mum was teaching me to swim."

David tells him : about the one he rescued, how I fed it on mince-meat
and hard-boiled egg, moistened with my saliva ; how I released it
& Tig pee into the sky, & how Olivia was close by me to see it go.
How sad we were, but how happy to think it might just get to Africa !

Tigger became more relaxed, happy and sleepy over a couple of days ; I wished
him well — the Otter Heaven. He was approaching his final hours & death with
dignity.

He had his last breakfast on the Sunday morning, more pills & was in
fact nearly asleep when his friend (Penny) the vet whom he had got to
know fairly well over his latter years finally put him to sleep as I held him
close. He was in no pain.

I told Storm that I left him (T) alone — his bed, as his spirits
departed this earth. I told her that all his pain had left his body
and how in sleep, although obviously much thinner, he looked his old
self — you could recognise the cheeky expression on his face !

74 Lachlan Street
Macquarie ACT 2614
Australia

25 October 1997

Dear David

What a thrill it was to meet you and Storm (and, of course, your lovely family); my grandfather, Bernard Smisson, would have been so happy to know that we'd met. I know he enjoyed his times with you very much.

When we arrived at your house, back on that cold February day, I honestly hadn't expected to meet a real, live otter! We knew you were interested in otters, and it was fascinating to talk to you over a cup of coffee about your work. Being an Australian, my only experience of otters was through British nature shows on television (as far as I know there aren't any in the wild here). So imagine my surprise and amazement when Mum and I followed you out into your backyard – and there was an OTTER!

She was beautiful! So alive, so happy – so inquisitive! She did not stop moving. She seemed to have boundless energy – into her pool, out again, racing around – and yet she was so fluid and graceful at the same time.

Being a cold, wintry day, we were all rugged up for the weather – including raincoats and my "beanie" (woolly hat with a pompom on top). As we sat down in Storm's yard, she came and investigated us – nosing, touching, running around – and then climbing all over us! Suddenly she found the pompom – a new toy! It seemed to delight her, and she sat on my head and shoulders to examine it more thoroughly.

It was exciting enough to see Storm up close, but to actually be able to touch her and have her play with us was mind blowing. Here was an animal who lived in the wild – yet who was so close. After we left you, Mum and I couldn't stop talking about Storm, and how amazing it was to be with her. It was a deeply moving experience, and one I will never forget. I feel privileged to have met her.

I am married now and have a baby of my own. I hope that he will one day experience the thrill of seeing an otter, and other wildlife, up close and in the wild. I believe your work for the otters and other wildlife is vital if we are to leave a good world for our children.

Thank you for your hospitality that day, and for being so welcoming, even though we were strangers. I wish you all the best in the future.

Love and best wishes to your family.

Yours sincerely

Sally Mordike (née Duncan) XXX

© J.B. Ridyard

La Lautron

I flow down stream
Down the young spring
Through reeds which shiver
In the wind

As I float through shimmering water
I dive down with a big splash
Suddenly my teeth sink into a fresh
water eel

As I twist down the current
The river becomes older and wiser
As the water seeps through my
webbed paws
I finally reach my destination the sea.

Yes I am an otter!!

Storm the Otter

Storm is an otter,
With a human mind
Some otters are fierce,
Some are kind.

A fresh water mammal,
Such beautiful creature
I really wish you could be mine.

You eat liver and eels,
And a whole lot more
Have you tried on heart?
Have you ever lived on a moor?

A fresh water mammal,
such a beautiful creature
I really wish you could be mine

You live in a holt
Made with mud, straw and twigs
Sometimes with cubs,
But not anymore.

by Olivia Chaffe
Aged 11

© J.B. Ridyard

'LANESIDE' HACKFORD, VALE, REEPHAM
NORWICH - NR10 4QU.

Dear David

My memories are mainly
of Fury - Taking her to the
North Norfolk coast for filming
she would do the whole journey
in the front of the Mini-pickup
lying on the passenger seat
or lying across my shoulders.
On one occasion at Morston
she swam out to sea until
she was just a speck in the
distance. We thought she was
making for Blakeney Point but
suddenly turned and came back.
She was such a gentle soul
never showed any aggression to
humans. Despite all this she
was a good breeding otter.

Hope to see you in the
near future - Love from us both

Roy + Diane

25th June

* Florn has many
similarities to Fury,
she's another......!
'gentle soul'
~~~~~~~~~~~

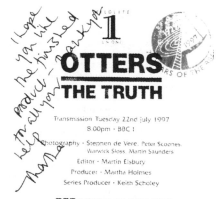

I hope
you will
produce the finished
product - thank you
for all your
help

1 BBC ONE

OTTERS
THE TRUTH

Transmission Tuesday 22nd July 1997
8.00pm · BBC 1

Photography · Stephen de Vere, Peter Scoones,
Warwick Sloss, Martin Saunders
Editor · Martin Elsbury
Producer · Martha Holmes
Series Producer · Keith Scholey

BBC NATURAL HISTORY UNIT

Alligator Creek
Amazonas
Brazil

October 14 1997

Dear David,

Having settled back into camp life out here in the rainforest I thought I would write to you (and Storm!) to bring you up to date on how filming is proceeding in this neck of the woods.

My eight brief weeks at home in the United Kingdom seem just a distant memory now. I do find it increasingly difficult to readjust to 'civilisation' there so perhaps after ten years I wonder if I have been out here too long.

We are in the grip of an extraordinary dry season – El Nino doing its best to make life even harder with just a few inches of water in our creek. At least we can still get drinking water from it although getting in and out for supplies is a trial. Yet it was marvellous paddling and pulling the canoe back up the creek on my return. One of the pleasures at this low water time is that it is not possible to use an outboard motor. This means that there is no noise to frighten the wildlife away. Hummingbirds whizzed about me and many other birds sang loudly as they found new flowering trees in the canopy overhead. A special sight I know that you will appreciate happened about half way up the creek as I was heading towards camp. A movement about twenty metres away caught my eye and there, in all her splendour, eating a Tucunare fish (one of my favourites too!) was a female southern river otter. She was perfectly lit by a shaft of sunlight breaking through the vegetation overhead and, even better, she had not seen me. I watched her for a good ten minutes before she slipped into the shallow crystal clear water and made her way further up stream. What a welcome back!

Like you, my life has been deeply affected by the delightful creatures. I shall never forget my first encounter with a wild otter, on the shores of the Isle of Mull. I moved up there in 1981 and during my first winter there I spent many days walking the coastline. He was a dog otter, fishing a few metres out from the shore of the loch and I ran down to lie in the seaweed to see if I could get a photograph of him when he next surfaced. Imagine how I felt when he surfaced with a large fish in his mouth and brought it ashore. But not just in front of me, he actually lay down next to me and his flank touched my frozen leg! He was too close to take a photograph and I wouldn't dare move anyway because one or both of us would have got a big shock. His teeth crunched through that fish – skull bone as well – with effortless ease. Only when he rolled over and away from my legs did he sense something and with a mighty 'huff' he galumphed back into the water where he simply carried on fishing. As I watched two hooded crows squabbling over some of the otter's left-overs, the whole landscape became bathed in that marvellous warm light that some special sunsets give out. Then I did get the photo I wanted.

Later that evening, back at my cottage, I was definitely not flavour of the month when I used my wife's cookware to dissolve and study the otter spraints that I had collected. I can conjure up that special 'ottery' smell in my mind right now – I really do like it. Does that make me strange?

After that experience the greatest coincidence was, of course, being sent out to Guyana in South America, to make my first Survival special – about otters, but of course they were a very different otter of our charming British species. I can never forget my first sight of a family of Brazilian Giant Otters. Over seven feet long and munching on piranha fish! What an experience. After those two years in Guyana I moved continents and thought that filming otters was over for a long while. My new home for the following two years was in the Gola Rainforest of Sierra Leone. My home was a tent on an uninhabited island in the middle of the Moa River. The stars of the film were to be primates. In fact eleven different species of them were all living in a forest of four square miles isolated on all sides by the fast flowing Moa River, it was a magical place. After only six weeks into the expedition I left the island early one morning with my daughter Emma (four years old at that time) to visit the chief of a village some two hours away by bush track. As we arrived we were besieged by fifty or more Mende people. In the midst of this small community I saw an old lady carrying a wicker basket to an open kitchen area. She pulled out a tiny dark brown furry bundle and although I didn't know what it was at that moment I certainly knew its fate, for in her other hand she held a large knife! I went over there quickly and asked what the animal was but didn't understand her reply. (I found out later that she had said 'Beef', the generic name for anything edible!) I picked the soft furry bundle up, it fitted into the palm of my hand, and I immediately realised that it was a new born African Spot Necked Otter.

The discovery that afternoon was to drastically change my lifestyle on Tiwai Island. I clearly couldn't let them eat him, he was a male and his eyes still unopened, so I somehow persuaded the lady to let me have him. He lived in my tent with me, slept in my hammock, constantly sprainted in it and kept two local lads from the nearest village fully employed every day to catch fish for him, for over a year! Emma named him Tum-Tum because to her that is all he seemed to think of, his tummy! As he grew up he explored the island and its waters on his own but always returned each afternoon for a swim with me in the river after I had finished work. Only once did his insatiable curiosity nearly cost him his life. I came across him snorting and huffing at the river's edge where only two feet from his nose was a very large python! He escaped with a bloodied nose and a healthy respect for snakes. He never did learn to catch fish for himself despite my frantic efforts to point them out to him underwater. He would chase them all day but never go in for that final kill. His favourite food were the river oysters there, cemented into the many rocks, and he did discover how to prize them off! What marvellous times I had with him.

I suppose it was Tum-Tum, meeting Storm and eventually another otter, 'Scottish' Sian, that fired an ambition to make a film about the European otter. As you know David, you and I have talked about this project late into many Cornish evenings, and even once while sitting with Storm. I still intend to do that film when I return to the UK, hopefully in 1999. I have been lucky enough to watch wild otters on Mull for many years and each and every single sighting, no matter how fleeting, is memorable of course. Diving under those west coast seas too I have often wondered if I would one day be lucky enough to come face to face with our passion! Well it was to happen but in an unexpected way.

My close friend, fellow wildlife enthusiast and photographer, Kip Halsey (he was with me when I first met Storm) called me one day to tell me of a local man who had a 'tame' otter on the Island. The result of meeting the couple who were raising Sian, Mr & Mrs John Weir, was that I spent two days under the sea in the Sound of Mull filming Sian as he hunted for crabs and fish. He was completely unafraid of my being there and for the most part ignored me. Underwater he was perfection itself. He even came up to my mask and pushed his nose into it!

Otters are of course, as we both know, beautiful on land but in their element, under the surface, they take on something else. Gliding, streaking with ballet-like movements and with a suppleness that I have never observed in any other animal. In short, they are living poetry. The moment he enters the water from the rocky shore-line his whole body is coated in liquid silver and this slowly loosens itself from his fur as he dives deeper. Wisps of bright bubbles rise above him and form curtains of air highlighted by the sunlight filtering through the surface a few metres above. What a stunning sight! Unforgettable.

So, in every way, otters have played an important part in my life and, thank heavens, continue to do so. I still film them from time to time out here in the Amazon for sequences in my films about the wildlife of this rainforest. Perhaps, though, the most special times are when I am alone in a canoe just paddling about and hear their screams and squabbles over a fish catch and then come face to face with the group. They are much more social than our British ones, sometimes as many as fifteen together! They surround my canoe for a good look at the stranger and huff and snort but other than that seem completely unafraid. This behaviour in the past has, of course, led to their serious decline. Thankfully the days of killing them for their fur are long gone and in some places I have come to know, far away from man, they seem to be recovering their numbers.

Now, it is late afternoon and almost 40 degrees. What heat! I have to go back into the forest to continue making my film about jaguars. It's proving to be difficult but slowly things are coming together. I had a marvellous sighting of a wild jaguar swimming across a wide river the other day. It sent tingles down my spine as I watched it clamber out on the other side, shake itself dry and disappear into the dark forest. I had finished my last roll of film earlier in the day and so couldn't capture it with my camera. That's wildlife filming for you!!

NEW MAILING ADDRESS:
Nick Gordon
c/Cavalcante
Rua Espirito Santo, 23
Bairro Lirio do Vale
CEP 69038 - 110
Manaus
Amazonas
BRAZIL

17.3.96.   Calcutta Cottage,
                                          Somerset.

Dear David

It was great to see both you + Storm last week. It
prompted me to think back over the seven years I have
known her.

My love of otters stems from reading Henry Williamson's
wonderful "Tarka" as a child. This inspired me to
try + see these secretive and elusive creatures for myself.
A good many years elapsed before I achieved this
ambition. Long hours were spent watching likely otter haunts
at dawn & dusk - often in damp & chilly conditions and
many long journeys were undertaken, especially to the
West coast of Scotland, where I thought my best chance
would be. Finally, I was rewarded by my first glimpse
of a wild otter, quite unexpectedly on a small beach by
the side of a fairly busy road, in the middle of the day
This, and subsequent sightings, were fairly fleeting but
tantalising, leaving me wanting to see more

So, when you invited me to meet Storm, I jumped at
the opportunity + feel very privileged to have been
able to watch her from the beginning.

When I first saw her, she was just a few weeks
old + could easily fit into my hand I was
immediately captivated by this tiny, trusting little
creature who allowed such a close encounter. Since then
I have spent many hours watching her, through various stages
of her development.

Seeing her recently, gliding sinuously through the water I
remembered her teetering timidly on the edge of her pool, running
a few steps this way & that, backwards & forwards, but not
daring to venture in. Soon after this, once she had discovered the joy of being an otter in her natural element
somersaulting + diving gracefully, playing with stones or
whatever else was at hand, she twice ran and clambered out
of her pool & up onto my lap where she proceeded to dry
herself vigorously. I thought this a wonderful compliment!

I am so grateful to you, David, for letting me spend
time with Storm - she really is a very special
little otter.

                    Take care.
                         Love, Hazel.
      from:
   ✳ HAZEL BIRKETT lngfune friend of Storm : see page 108; \ 17.3.49.

Veterinary pathologist Vic Simpson has never seen an otter in the wild, but years of research show that these nocturnal mammals are far from extinct in the South West.

Otters are his silent witnesses, brought for post mortem examinations to his Ministry of Agriculture laboratory at Polwhele on the outskirts of Truro from across the region by the Environment Agency.

Otters have occupied Mr Simpson's thoughts for the past 10 years and his work has pinpointed the likely reasons for the otters decline to near extinction from 1957 onwards and evidence of a recovery in the 1990s.

Mr Simpson says, "it's mostly good news, with much less chemical pollution in streams and rivers in recent years but serious threats to otters remain in the form of future road, industrial and housing developments. My research from 1988 to 1998 shows that otters in the South West are well nourished and not suffering from significant infectious diseases. However, mortality due to road traffic is a major problem and fighting between otters is the second most common cause of death."

Mr Simpson looks for signs of infection and illness likely to be caused by pollutants flowing into water courses and entering the otters' food chain.

"Tissue analysis over this period has shown that the chemicals which are widely believed to have caused the population crash are declining every year with demonstrable benefits to otters health."

Although there is still no definite proof, Mr Simpson as many other scientists, suspects that the agricultural and industrial pesticide Dieldrin, marketed during the 1950s has been a principal cause of the otters' decline. He concludes, "we cannot be sure exactly what has been and is going on, but I don't think that it is coincidental that the otter population has visibly improved since Dieldrin became prohibited in the late 1980s.

bring home this point in Hampole story

Dear David

from James Williams Esq. North Somerset Jan '99

Storm cannot know it, but on the hilly and turbulent stream where she so nearly came to grief all those years ago, a few wild otters are still living. Modern life can be difficult for an otter: a young bitch otter was run over in autumn 1998, not far from where Storm was rescued. Her body was found by the same postman who saved Storm.

But there are still others to carry on Storm's family. Nobody sees them, but there is a fallen ash tree one field from where she was found, which regularly carries fresh spraints, and the stone drain from which she was almost certainly washed by the storm which gave her her name is still smoothly polished.

I'm looking forward to the book

Yrs James

\# These two letters tie in with the tendril at one of Storm's Hinkley letmes (2-3 years previously) also reported regularly leaving an unidentifiable whining — to stream close to her Shustin home. After leaving Storm she knew it was an otter/often calling! I did Phonic notice from the same stream tirsit since.

Hinkley Point, Somerset.
26 February, 1999

Dear David,

Some encouraging news!

On a recent scout around the Nature Trail here I discovered mammal tracks leading out of a rhyne. With visions of Storm still in focus from her visit here, I hoped fervently that these were otter tracks and perhaps even those of one of Storm's distant relatives.

The following day, James Williams examined the many tracks and confirmed that a large dog otter has been working this area regularly. We even found a bank where he had playfully rolled and scratched. This site is several miles from known otter population centres in the Brue and Tone valleys and it may be some 15 years since otters frequented what James has until now called 'the Bridgwater gap'. Storm might find these plain rhynes and expanses of flat moor uninspiring and the sea here murky but few roads cross this habitat so the risk of otters being run over is low.

Next day I took a fresh spraint sample for DNA analysis. It is a long shot, but it might indicate whether 'our' otter has come from either of the populations already under observation. Either way, I shall be watching with interest.

My regards to you, Storm, Olivia and Helen,

John.

John Burrell Esq, Reserve Warden, Hinkley Point 'A'

MARTIN H. SMITH
TICKETYBOO COTTAGE
NORTH NORFOLK.

Dear David

It was a great pleasure to meet you and work with Storm on the river film in Norfolk, which had many other characters along the river bank I.e. water vole, kingfisher, swans, warblers and the main character being that of the Little Grebe, Storm just put the finishing touch to the film I am very greatful for your help and assistance, and look forward to working with you again in the future.

All the best from

Martin, Pauline and Megan.

Further K The brennum year film (Nov 98) and above, have returned yet again to North Norfolk and, in particular, to the Stiffkey and hennum mers K complete some sequences with storm and Martin, this time for the BBC's N H Units forthcoming 'LIVING BRITAIN'

Produced by Peter Crawford, the 6 x 50 min progs are scheduled for BBC 2 late autumn '99.

Subscribers

Sue Almey	Nailsea, North Somerset
Babs Beynon	Hereford
John and Wendy Carlin	Brent Knoll, Somerset
Anne and Peter Chouler	Scarborough, N. Yorkshire
David Cobham	King's Lynn, Norfolk
Jan. H. de Vries	Marazion, Cornwall
Geoff Doran B.V.Sc., M.R.C.V.S.	Thornbury, Bristol
Brenda and Trevor Downes	St. Ives, Cornwall
Joan and Alan Dowsett	Redland, Bristol
Anna Duval	Greenbank, Bristol
Tim and Liz Frazer	Curry Rivel, Somerset
Malcolm Gilbert	St. Ives, Cornwall
Ray Hancock	Kilve, Somerset
Andrea Harrington	Easter Compton, Bristol
Benjamin and Eleanor Hattersley	High Wycombe, Bucks
Eric and Pat Hembrow	Stoke St. Gregory, Somerset
Colin and Olive Holdom	Berrow, Somerset
Bob and Barbara Hunt	Nether Stowey, Somerset
Mike James	Blagdon, North Somerset
Tony Jennings	Cholsey, Oxon
Pauline Kidner	East Huntspill, Somerset
Jackie Lucas	Hinkley Point, Somerset
Stephanie Mears	Blagdon, North Somerset
Bill and Grace Nafzger	Westbury-on-Trym, Bristol
John Nettles	Evesham, Worcs
John Pallent	Portishead, North Somerset
Pat and Ernest Pallent	Gwinear, Cornwall
John and Elaine Poppy	Davidstow, Cornwall
Ray and Sally Proctor	Bampton, Oxon
Liz Rapson	Camborne, Cornwall
Chris and Margo Sampson	Winscombe, Somerset
Chris and Sally Searle	Boscastle, Cornwall
Bill Slee M.R.C.V.S.	Torbridge Vet Centre, Bideford
John Thomas	St. Ives, Cornwall
Michael Tucker	Barnstaple, Devon
Sandra Vincent	Carmarthen
Paul Walkden	Sharpness, Glos
Sylvia Watts	Clevedon, North Somerset
West Buckland School	Barnstaple, Devon
Stan, Rose and Penny Woods	St. Ives, Cornwall
Norman and Audrey Woollon	Lower Langford, North Somerset

OTTER

An otter am I,
High and dry
Over the pebbles
See me hobble.
My water-bag wobbles
Until I spill
At the river sill
And flow away thin
As an empty skin
That dribbles bubbles

Then I jut up my mutt,
All spikey with wet.
My moustaches bristle
As I mutter, or whistle:
"Now what's the matter?"

(For that is my song.
Not very long.
There might be a better
Some wetter, wittier
Otter could utter.)

I hope you have enjoyed 'Stormforce' and will want to act positively for otters and the wild places where they live.

Storm and I, along with my close friend Malcolm Sayer, have recently completed two successful filming forays to north Norfolk. Martin Smith was cameraman on both occasions both for Survival's 'The Treasure Year,' and the NH Unit's 'Living Britain' series. Who could have imagined that Storm would be filmed on the Treasure and Stiffkey rivers, so close in otter 'mileage' to those very marshes where my first cub was found over thirty years ago; the marshes to which the wild otters have returned to live and which they share with the wild geese in winter.

Storm is now living close to the River Torridge, close to her grandmother's territory where her mother may have spent the first formative months of her life. Storm can hear the calls of the wild otter. The wheel has, indeed, turned full circle.

Yet again, late last night, I spent quality time with Storm. I told her that 'Stormforce' was now completed, and that hopefully, very soon, people everywhere will be reading her story. I reminded her that, once heard, her name will never be forgotten.

"I'll miss the snipe toing and froing from the tussock sedge in the reedbed on winter days, and pond-side at dusk, the water rails grunting like little piglets. They were fun. However, there are buzzards, ravens and curlews here, and it appears, a large family of wrens, too, living in the cavities and crannies of the wall next to my den."

No doubt these familiar sounds would trigger many vivid memories for Storm.

"By the way," she concluded, "don't forget to tell everybody — it's our world, too!"

"I will Storm, I promise."

Weare Giffard, North-west Devon.
Saturday night, 31st July '99.

I know that the reader will allow me, in the days and weeks ahead, to personally thank the many people who have contributed to my spending thirty years plus with otters, and to recording some of those times in this book.

However, there are several persons who, sadly, have predeceased the publication of *Stormforce* and it would be remiss of me not to record my debt to them at this time. By mentioning their names, no further explanation is necessary.

They include Bernard and Peggy Smisson, S.P.T. Wells, Robin Jones, Ted Hughes, John Cooksley, whose beautiful sketches adorn the chapter headings, and especially but most recently, Nancy, my dear mother.

"Some clever person once said that the world is divided into two kinds of people. Those who divide the world into two kinds of people and those who don't. You'll know which group I belong to if I suggest that the world may be divided into those who care and those who don't. It's because I belong to the first group in that division that I am so enormously thrilled and honoured to receive this prize."

The words above are those of Sir Peter Scott, the founder of the Wildfowl and Wetlands Trust, at Slimbridge in Gloucestershire, on being presented with the International Pahlavi Environment Prize on the 3rd June 1977 at the United Nations in New York.

Later Sir Peter continued, "I have been worried by the increasing rate of species extinction, species that are the current end product of 30 million centuries, three thousand million years of evolution since life began on Earth. Many of them have been wiped out in a mere instant of geological time, through the ignorance, carelessness and greed of mankind. . . and it's still going on."

Sir Peter Scott is widely regarded as the 'Father of Conservation'. His pioneering dreams continue to inspire me and other naturalists and wildlife projects worldwide.

THE COMMEMORATION OF AN IDYLL

JOURNEY'S END
AND AN APPROPRIATE LEGACY FOR STORM

There is, at present, an emptiness, a sense of desolation, in part of my everyday life. By ten o'clock most nights, Sasha our English springer spaniel and Shadow, Olivia's golden retriever bitch, will have slipped out of doors for one last exercise. This will be the point in time, too, when most sensible people will, in their own special ways, prepare for the night ahead.

However, at this time a while back, I would be venturing outside whatever the time of year or however inclement the weather. I would be going to visit my wild bitch otter, Storm. She was my friend and loyal companion and we would be meeting for our late-night fun together.

I would approach her enclosure through the utility room at the rear of our cottage. A large picture window provided an immediate view of what Storm was doing at any time of the day or night. She, not surprisingly, possessed as good a time clock as Sasha who can somehow predict the very moment I am deciding to take her out just before I move from my chair. I would usually find Storm loitering on the straw bales which lay alongside her freshwater tank or already rolling effortlessly in the crystal clear water. The moment I switched on the lights or eased the first of the bolts on the entrance door to her enclosure, she would raise her tempo. She would plunge and roll with much more urgency and would chase backwards and forwards. Such was her wholehearted welcome for me.

The fully-lined hut was her domain, her territory as well as her sleeping quarters, her artificial and snug holt. Inside was a much smaller tank and one of Storm's two identical travelling crates in which she always slept on an assorted pile of my old sweaters and bathtowels. Alongside was a chair where I was allowed to sit! Most nights I would wait for fully half an hour or more for Storm to finish her play.

As the years had passed Storm had become ever more active at night time. It seemed she was reverting to her natural and wild instincts. Her den was also fitted with electric light and infra-red heating. It was from this 'inner sanctum' that she travelled on her long journeys under special licence from English Nature and it was to here that she always returned after any public or filming work. Whilst waiting for her to decide to join me, I would settle into my writing, outlining perhaps the text of personal letters.

Eventually Storm would appear and inevitably would be dripping wet. She would pause at the entrance and at the same time shimmer, thus discarding the excess water from her outer coat as she crossed the threshold. Next she would urinate and deposit her spraint on the heavy duty mat which was immediately adjacent to the door. I would take this mat with Storm on all her outings, ensuring when on location it was always available adjacent to her travelling crate. Without fail she would mark the mat both when leaving the crate and when returning. This was often several hours later and I soon learnt that this final action also indicated the ending of any further activities for the day.

Once inside, Storm would linger for a few moments before suddenly rushing towards me at speed. In one movement she would jump into my lap, pausing only momentarily, before springing again higher and across me onto a thick bathtowel. This would be draped across the top of her den. She would immediately start to dry herself thoroughly, rolling, twisting and turning with great energy. For the meantime I would ignore her and continue to write.

I would realise the remarkable affection of my otter when, a while later, I would first sense the gentle touch of her whiskers and then feel her wet nose pressing against the skin on the back of my neck and behind my ears. Now was certainly not the time to suddenly alter my position. I had to allow Storm to continue exploring even if she did occasionally nibble an ear. The coarse-textured fisherman's smocks, sensible and essential clothing worn at any time when in Storm's company, were well impregnated with her body odours. Storm would force her head and shoulders into the open neck to try and squeeze down my chest via the inside of my shirt, or would push around a shoulder in order to force herself down my back.

Some nights she would become rather annoyed by her lack of progress and inability to explore further. Now this was yet another time to stay very still and I always tried to make light of any exploratory nips. Was Storm putting my patience to the test? Was she remembering the first late nights of play as a tiny cub under the infra-red lamp when her favourite game was to chase the length of sash-cord amongst the scattered straw bales? Or was she letting me know, in her own particular way, just who was boss? Whatever, any such encounter inevitably preceded the next but very predictable step in her nightly behaviour.

Storm was now quite ready to curl herself into a tight ball in my lap to go to sleep. In no time I would be listening to her gentle snoring. Sometimes I would just move slightly to avoid becoming stiff and occasionally I would stop my writing to gently stroke her muzzle and the top of her head. Sometimes I would rest my clipboard on her back. She would take no notice; she was completely comfortable with her closeness to me but any adjustment on my part simply prompted yet another slight twisting of her body. The end result was, inevitably, one upside down otter!

There is no doubt that Storm always planned to remain stationary for some time. It was up to me to make the final move and by then it would often be well past midnight. Gently I would lift Storm on top of the crate and back into the thick and shaggy textures of the towel. When I returned from indoors with her food, which I would have prepared earlier, plus a replacement dry towel, she would be waiting for me at the entrance of her enclosure. She would scamper ahead of me and would always feed in exactly the same place. She would try to take the first pieces before her bowl had touched the floor and would tuck in as if she had not seen food for days! A mixture of ox-heart, pig's liver and either small silver or sand eels were her favourites, but a special treat was the roe from a grey mullet.

I was able to obtain a few of these fish from time-to-time after they had been traditionally netted close to the old Long Bridge that spans the River Torridge in Bideford. A life-long resident of Weare Giffard, Mary Hedden, has told me that her mother would give her money to buy the family fresh mullet when walking home from school. The fish would have been caught close to the village's Halfpenny Bridge and would cost three or four old pence each. Mary's mother would gut and clean the fish, leaving them standing in fresh water for twenty-four hours before cooking them in bacon fat. The head-end of the fish had more bones than the tail portion so brothers and sisters took turns over servings. Mary can remember on some occasions seeing so many grey mullet in the still water at the top of the tide, where the fresh waters pouring out of the heartland of north-west Devon had met the incoming tidal surge from the northern Atlantic Ocean, that she felt she could have walked across the river on the backs of the fish. No wonder otters have found these fish-rich waters so attractive since time immemorial.

Storm, whilst still eating, would watch me leave out of the corner of an eye. Some nights, however, I would stay to watch and check her through the hut window. To mislead her, to make her believe I had finally gone, I would bang the enclosure door shut without sliding the bolts into position. Storm would finish her meal, would use her sprainting mat one last time and then would quickly venture into her travelling crate. Strangely as she turned to make herself snug, she would always let out a subdued cry, a final whimper that would be clearly audible in the stillness of the night. Who was she calling? With whom was she trying to communicate?

A final flick of a switch would eliminate all the outside lights, including those in her den, and I would leave my enchanting creature. She was close, very close in terms of the distances that otters can and do travel, to the River Torridge and not far from Halspill Creek in the parish of Weare Giffard, somewhere in the Land of the Two Rivers.

I would often think as I made my way upstairs past Olivia's bedroom that somehow Storm knew that she had finally come with us to a very special place. She would end her days here, by the rough moors, the water meadows and tidal creeks that had forged the territories and holts of her wild grandparents.

© Gabrielle Bordewich

Throughout the autumn of '99 Storm, Olivia and I completed many interviews together as the publication date for *Stormforce* loomed ever closer. Olivia and Storm were very excited as they posed for pictures together. Olivia was always reserved but Storm was, by now, conscious of the camera.

The highlight undoubtedly was the visit of the Daily Mail's June Southworth who had most kindly accepted my invitation to meet Storm. She overnighted at the Imperial Hotel in Barnstaple so as to spend a full day with us as a family. Here was a Fleet Street columnist and feature writer of high renown. She had accompanied the wildlife artist David Shepherd to the game reserves of East Africa. By contrast, she was one of a handful of western journalists who were on the ground at the fall of Saigon.

Immediately fascinated and clearly captivated by Storm she was quickly aware, too, of Storm's very close bond with Olivia. She was anxious to capture that relationship, using it to form the structure of her article and so, astutely, spent most of the afternoon alone with our daughter. The result, later that week, was a centre-spread feature illustrated in colour which reflected Olivia's close friendship with Storm. It also revealed the immediate trust that Olivia placed in someone who, until their meeting, was a total stranger. She had subtly elicited from Olivia her attachment to Storm and had evoked Olivia's spontaneous responses such as "she [Storm] was like a sister to me".

I shall always be grateful to June Southworth's endorsement of Storm's remarkable and true story and of the many otter characters whose lives we had enjoyed within our extended family. Those individuals and their successful cubbings contributed much to my lifetime's work with, and achievements for, one of the world's most thrilling species. The Mail's story ensured that the early sales of *Stormforce* were given a remarkable boost nationwide. The telephone didn't stop ringing for four days! Alison McDougall, the Mail's freelance photographer, had also captured a never to be forgotten moment that momentous Tuesday. She secured, from countless shots, the best ever picture of Storm and Olivia together. That portrait, preciously claimed and reflecting the occasion, is the highlight of the back cover of this paperback.

Storm and I continued to carry out a range of conservation presentations which fulfilled the ongoing exemption originally granted by English Nature that Storm 'should be used for scientific and educational purposes.' In early December we attended a combined Dorset and Wiltshire Wildlife Trusts and South West, Wessex and Southern Waters presentation at the Dorset Trust's Kingcombe Meadows Reserve near Toller Porcurum close to Dorchester. The RSPB and English Nature were also represented.

After an initial introduction by Lisa Schneidau, the national director of the Otters and Rivers Project, Professor David Bellamy was invited to coordinate the work of the various Agencies. With his customary directness and enthusiasm he was soon bringing home the relevant issues to the gathered media. A successful photo shoot with Storm was quickly completed and when the critical topic of water quality had to be addressed, he promptly discarded shoes and socks to make his message clearly understood from the centre of the stream. At the riverbank, where an artificial otter holt for eventual use by the wild otters using the valley had been partially completed, a second photo-session took place. The holt was one of several planned for this brook which is a tributary of the River Hooke. The latter meanders through traditional and precious wet water-meadows which have remained untouched for six hundred years. Artificial chemicals have never been applied and the excess summer vegetation is still not controlled by mechanical hedging flails.

Come the new Millennium, Storm and I and her friend Malcolm Sayer, who was with us in Dorset, were away again, this time filming for BBC Television in the bleak Northumberland countryside. Storm was by now a seasoned traveller, well accustomed to all the routines; the story-line was that she was to represent a wild otter recovering from injury; she quickly completed the required sequences with many natural and spontaneous close-ups coordinated by Paul Tormey from the programme and Kevin O'Hara of the Northumberland Wildlife Trust. However, we were soon hurrying home to the much milder climes of the Torridge valley, and I continued to promote and successfully sell the hardback *Stormforce* nationwide.

Olivia and I were not to realise that Storm's last two public performances would take place on consecutive days, the 23rd and 24th of March. She was to feature at West Buckland School in north Devon. This was a particularly poignant occasion for Olivia, as she is a pupil at the school.

The following afternoon, within the confines of Storm's own enclosure and surrounded by all her familiar furniture, the three of us enjoyed personal interviews with Liz Scott of BBC Radio Devon. As with everyone else that Storm allowed into her home territory, Liz Scott was charmed by her affection, but was reminded from time to time of her inherent wildness, and certainly when alongside Storm as she 'porpoised' in her tank. It was a fresh spring afternoon with all that the North Devon farmland and countryside hereabouts has to offer in springtime, but little did we know that by the time of the broadcast, Storm would no longer be with us.

Next up was the launch of the Welsh Wildlife Trust's Otters and Rivers Project with Welsh Water near Bridgend in South Wales with an invitation to meet the guests of honour, the Minister of State for the Environment for the Welsh Assembly, Sue Essex, and Howie Watkins, one of the presenters from BBC1's *Really Wild Show*. Storm was also to be introduced to a group of local primary school children and I could imagine their excited anticipation at the prospect of meeting a live British otter 'face-to-face'.

However, the ending of her remarkable life happened very quickly.

Seventy-two hours beforehand, Storm would not, could not, eat her evening meal. I rang and forewarned Ceri Rogers, who was the Trust's co-ordinator, to tell him I had fingers crossed. However, I already knew that the final scenes of an era were about to occur, – and sooner rather than later. I am still unable, two years later, to describe the intimate moments and emotions that I shared with Storm during that last weekend. I was always aware that such a dreadful day would eventually dawn from those first tense and emotive times in February '92 when Storm was being bottle-fed. Against the odds Storm, my family and eventually thousands of people, including many youngsters, would cherish her eventual survival. We and they have all taken away lifetime memories of the world natural from being in her close presence.

I had lost other individual otters; all had departed leaving me with precious recollections of their own distinctive personalities. I had found every occasion painful. But I had never held another otter close, never been able to gently stroke another otter's muzzle and forehead in the way I did with Storm and which I can still do now many times a day with Sasha and Shadow. Life with Storm was such a privilege, an indescribable adventure in the confidence of a wild creature and more especially of a wild otter. I miss her companionship terribly and no words can describe her loss.

I was with my ailing otter at the end of her life, very late on Monday April 3rd. That was the day she should have been exciting the Welsh audience and media, with Storm and I stating the case that wild otters continue to fly red danger signals for wetland environments and for the need to monitor levels of water quality. In 1962 Dr Don Jefferies had initiated his first post-mortem work on otters whose tissues and organs were suspected of having high accumulations of organochlorine insecticides. They were soon identified as DDT and lindane, and the more toxic dieldrin and aldrin, persistent in the soils of eastern England and in the sheep dips in Wales and the West.

Now, fifty years later, a recovery in the wild population is well under way. By 2002 the otters of the South West should have re-occupied 75% of their waterways. However an increase of 75% over the whole of England is unlikely before the year 2025, 70 years after the decline started. Don Jefferies writes that conservationists should learn to recognise that they will never know when the next problem is going to occur. He reminded me so in a personal letter, (March '02), where he wrote that 'the otter population is still vulnerable'.

Firstly, there is a very high and increasing level of road mortality; otters will get out of rivers and cross the road when coming to bridges rather than face the rapid currents underneath them – serious in winter spate conditions. Secondly, there is the possibility of a wildlife disease epizootic. Phocene Distemper Virus killed 50% of the common seals off the Norfolk coast in 1988. (Now, PDV has been confirmed in five common seals at a North Norfolk RSPCA rescue centre at King's Lynn – 12/08/02. Two thousand are already dead in Northern Europe). As Jefferies points out the otter is antagonistic to the mink, the diseases of one could be transferred to the other by fighting. We should be determined, therefore, to be ensuring with ever more vigilance that the otter's present recovery continues in the wild places where they should be living.

I had taken Storm in her travelling crate the few hundred yards from our house to Halspill Creek. For one last time she was able to see the Land of the Two Rivers. I knew this would mean so much to her and I held her weak body tight to mine. As her wild grandmother did before, she listened to the sounds of the river and the distinctive cries of the wild birds. She was still strong enough to lift her head, turning into the breeze to smell the incoming sea-tide.

She heard the shelducks courting, as the drakes advanced on one another. By early June crèches of their ducklings would be scampering over the exposed mud with a mother-duck at either end of the groups. Meanwhile, pairs of common teal, curlew and redshank were lost amongst the black-headed gulls who were there in force, but all were discussing when they should leave for their nesting grounds on the high moors and where Storm's wild mother so enjoyed their company.

"No sign of an early swallow or house martin yet," whispered Storm.

"Only another few days now before the first stragglers are resting and recharging at Netherdown Farm up the lane," I replied, hardly able to contain my sadness.

"I still have my family of wrens though," Storm continued, remembering how much these little birds meant to her family when at Christmas-time all those years ago Storm was born one of triplets in the wild holt on Exmoor. "They will be waiting for me you know, when you take me home. . . they're always there for me. . . but first let's stay here for a while. . ."

It was much later that evening that Storm finally went to sleep for the last time. I stayed with her well into the early hours.

I have always found it difficult to précis Storm's life and her impact on my family. I believe I came close when I had the honour of replying to guests at a dinner in the Fortescue Hotel, Barnstaple as *Stormforce* received the non-fiction award for 2001 from the Associated Independent Publishers.

I chose as my theme synonyms for the word 'chance' taken from the Concise Oxford Thesaurus. My notes are recorded below.

Was it (FATE) when a coastguard's sp/sp fetched my first orphaned otter cub off the north Norfolk marshes on Boxing Day '66? — when my lifetime with otters began.

Was it (LUCK) when a postman on Exmoor in Feb '92, rescued the 1lb 7ozs casualty of a rough winter night? — and just before the milk tanker squeezed up the lane at first light.

Was it 'S (FORTUNE) that no one responded to the postman's urgent tel/calls for assistance until 24 hrs later when my wife Helen was the first to react positively?

Was it a (COINCIDENCE) that Storm then joined the only private and breeding collection of British otters in the UK and was granted a one-off exemption by E/N for scientific and educational work?

Was it a (COINCIDENCE), too, that she found an a young companion, our daughter Olivia? Both contributed so much to each other and I have recorded these events with much pleasure throughout the text of SF. Why did Olivia tell the DM's JS on the publication of SF that (quote) 'Storm was like a sister to me.'

Was it S' (DESTINY) to become known nationwide? Will her remarkable and true story become her destiny in memoriam?

There is no more to say now; Storm is in the world to which all otters strive to reach. She knew that her two companions, Pebble and Ripple, were still breeding well at the Otter Trust's Tamar Sanctuary in North Cornwall (at least fifteen cubs now by mid-summer '02) and that one day they would both join her again and share their ottery secrets.

So, I will conclude this true story with my final notes from the Awards evening. I know they will suffice.

Will Storm's story become a resource and essential cross-curricular reading for Years 6 & 7 & 8 pupils nationwide? Hence the paperback edition planned for the autumn of '02.

And will those youngsters take on board the real and crucial messages of Storm's story . . . . to love nature . . . — and to love life !

"The world is as delicate and as complicated as a spider's web. If you touch one thread, you send shudders running through all the other threads. We're not just touching the web – we're tearing great holes in it."

Reprinted with permission of Curtis Brown Group Ltd
on behalf of the Estate of Gerald Durrell

©Gerald Durrell

Storm © Gabrielle Bordewich

**born on Exmoor sometime
between Christmas Day and
New Years Eve December 1991
passed away Weare Giffard,
North Devon, April 3rd 2000**

An appropriate legacy for Storm

I want ever more readers to share Storm's experiences and I particularly want to see young people at school nationwide in Years 6 & 7 and 8 & 9 challenged to create their own projects based on *Stormforce*. Cross-curricular, their studies would be of lasting value and would meet many of the criteria of Key Stages 2 and 3 of the National Curriculum.

Would you help ensure the legacy of the marvellous wild creature, Storm? Are you, or do you know of a potential contributor, who might give copies to a school local to you? We must all be concerned with raising the level of environmental knowledge and responsibility of our youngsters. *Stormforce, an otter's tale* deserves to be part of that awareness in the classroom and is already being welcomed as it finds its place in those schools which are concerned to educate and not merely to instruct.

If you have any suggestions or want further information for making this paperback edition available to schools please write to me at:

Stormforce Publications, Little Weare Cottage
Weare Giffard, Devon EX39 4QZ

or email me at: davidchaffe.stormforcebooks@virgin.net

At Christmas-time all those years ago, Storm was born one of triplets in the wild holt on Exmoor.

You do take my life when you do take the means whereby I live.

William Shakespeare,
Merchant of Venice